What causes a teenager to turn to crime? Peer pressure? The frustrations of poverty? An unstable home environment? In the case of sixteen-year-old Sherri Lenier, it was all of these, and more. Tasting the thrills and excitement of shoplifting, Sherri went on to become a sophisticated theft artist with the world at her fingertips—and the underworld on her back. Only when the cell door clanked shut did she discover the real victim of her crimes—herself. Here is a captivating story of a young woman's desperate search for lasting peace and security... of the stark realities of sin and its consequences ... and of her surrender to the One who alone could satisfy her deepest longings. Ultimately, SHERRI represents the spiritual journey of every one of us.

BY John Benton

Sherri

JOHN BENTON

SPIRE 🏛 BOOKS

Fleming H. Revell Company
Old Tappan, New Jersey

Scripture references in this volume are from the King James Version
of the Bible.

Library of Congress Cataloging in Publication Data

Benton, John, date
  Sherri

  I. Title.
PZ4.B4788Sh [PS3552.E57]   813'.54   80-14480
ISBN 0-8007-8390-5

This is an original Spire book, published by Spire Books, a division
of Fleming H. Revell Company, Old Tappan, New Jersey.

TO Mildred Rogers, whose love and dedication mean so much to Elsie, me, and all our girls.

Sherri

1

I bounced up the front stairs of our porch, my mind on—what else?—*food!* After pushing hard all day at school, I knew that a peanut-butter-and-jam sandwich would carry me through until Mom had supper ready. Loaded with calories? Yeah, but I shoved that out of my mind. I certainly wasn't that much overweight: ten pounds, maybe. I promised myself I'd start that diet— tomorrow. After all, I'd die, if I didn't get something to eat right now!

Juggling three textbooks, notebook, purse, and gym shoes, I finally grabbed the doorknob and turned. Drat! Stuck again! I shoved the door with my shoulder, then shoved harder. Suddenly it moved. I caught myself, but my books went splattering to the floor. First I swore, then I bent down to pick them up. My algebra book seemed to mock me, so I spit on it. I couldn't see any possible purpose in having to study a . . . .

"Sherri!" My mother's shrill voice irritated me even more. "Sherri! Did you just do what I think you did?"

"Aw, come on, Mom. You told me how much you hated algebra when you were in high school."

"Never mind that. You should show more respect for your textbooks. You can't always do what you want to do. Part of school is learning to . . . ."

"Oh, well, one more year after this year, and school's all over for little, sweet Sherri," I interrupted. "No more studies. No more getting up at six.

I'll be on my own—free as a bird!''

Just thinking about it made me feel better. Here I was, sixteen. Next year I'd be a senior. As soon as I could after I graduated, I was going to move out of this dump. We lived on the wrong side of town, and, so help me, I wasn't going to live in this kind of poverty forever. I had plans to live in a big, beautiful brick home, with all the good things of life at my fingertips. I wasn't sure how it was going to happen, but I was going to do it!

I grabbed all my things and kicked the door shut.

"Shhh," Mom told me. "Dad's home." She pointed toward the kitchen.

"Is Dad sleeping in the kitchen?"

"Shut up in there!" he yelled.

I suspected what it was, but I threw my books on the sofa and marched into the kitchen. One quick look told me the whole story. Dad, bleary eyed, looked up at me. Six empty beer bottles sat on the kitchen table—it probably hadn't taken him long to down them. Drunk again.

I looked down on him disdainfully. "You're disgusting, Dad," I said as calmly as I could, under the circumstances. "Absolutely disgusting!"

He raised his head. When his eyes met mine, he started to whimper. "Oh, Sherri; I'm sorry. Real sorry."

Saliva formed in my mouth, and I beat back the impulse to spit in his face. I hated him more than I hated algebra. Everyone in school knew I had a drunk for a father. It was so embarrassing.

Then he began to bawl. Big tears splashed down his cheeks, and I knew that he would begin to explain, as he had hundreds of times before, that he didn't know what came over him. Now all I could do was pity him.

I heard Mom sobbing in the living room. She especially needed me now, so I eased onto the sofa, next to her. How many times had I done this to comfort her? Many times, when my father had beaten her, or when they'd had a terrible argument. I even remembered when she and I had to go out onto the front porch and pick Dad up and carry him into the house, because he was so drunk. I knew then that all our neighbors were peering out their windows at us. I died a little on the inside.

Now, as I slipped my arm around my mother, I asked, "Why—this time?"

"He got fired."

"Fired? What happened?"

"Well, this time it really wasn't his fault. The company is having financial problems. The boss told him this morning that they just had to cut back. Your father didn't have any seniority, so he was the first to go."

"But can't he get another job?"

"Are you kidding? He has no skills and no education. There are ten men for every unskilled-labor job available. His drinking problem doesn't make it any easier for him. I guess we'll just have to do the best we can."

"What do you mean, the best we can? He'll get unemployment, won't he? Something will turn up."

Mom started sobbing again. "No, Sherri, no unemployment. His company didn't provide it. We'll have to go on welfare again."

"For crying out loud!" I exploded. "Don't you have any idea what this does to me? All the kids at school

looked down on me when my old man was on welfare
before. You promised me, when we went off welfare,
that I'd never have to suffer that embarrassment again!
Don't you remember?''

Now I was the one bawling. I buried my face in her
lap.

"Now calm down, Sherri," she said lovingly, as
she stroked my hair. "I meant what I promised. I
really thought your father was going to go straight and
things would turn out all right. I can't help it if he lost
his job. So don't blame me.''

I figured Mom was covering up for him again. I was
sure that the real reason he got fired was that he was
drunk on the job—again.

That's the way it had been before. My dad was an
alcoholic, and he couldn't hold any job more than a
few weeks.

I pushed myself up from her lap and looked into her
face. "Oh, Mom," I wailed, "what are we going to do?
Do you really have to go down and get in that line at
the welfare department?''

"Listen, Sherri, don't you think it's about time you
started to think about how I feel? Do you think I enjoy
standing in that line? Do you know how I feel, when
the postman brings the welfare check and grins smugly
as he hands it to me? I know what people think. They
think we're a bunch of lazy, good-for-nothing bums,
living off the government. I hate it as much as you hate
it, maybe more. But I'm trapped. I can't do a thing
about it!''

Between sobs, she went on: "I've tried to be a good
wife to your father. I believe in honesty and all the
virtues a wife is supposed to have. When things got

tough, I just gritted my teeth and made the best of it. But I don't think I can take this much longer."

Just then, Dad appeared in the doorway, staggering toward us. Instinctively, I stood up. He wasn't usually violent when he was drunk, but I knew I had to be ready—just in case.

"Come on, you two crybabies," he blubbered. "Ever'thin' ish gonna be okay. Jus' a few days, and I'll be back to work. So don' you two worry 'bout one little thing."

I was so sick of his continual false hopes. Nothing was ever going to be any better. That's why I couldn't wait to get away from home.

He moved unsteadily, to about a foot from me. "Sherri, li'l darlin', you're the best daughter any father could have. Do you really love your ole Daddy?"

Oh, no! Not one of his hugging moods! I couldn't stand the sight of him—much less the smell. As he lurched forward, I easily sidestepped him. He lost his balance and sprawled on the floor.

I stared down at him in utter disgust. I don't think he even knew why he had fallen. He simply rolled to his side and tried to get up on one knee. Then he fell again. Mom finally came to his rescue.

Mom looked up at me, her eyes red from crying. "Sherri, can't you answer your father?" she demanded.

I bit my tongue. What I wanted to say was something no father should ever hear from his daughter— not even if he is drunk. So, without a word, I turned and headed for the kitchen. Now I really needed that sandwich.

I opened the refrigerator, looking where Mom usually kept the bread. None! Just my luck. Mom didn't have that much to do. Why couldn't she have gone to the store for some bread?

"Mom," I called, "do we have any more bread?"

No answer.

I walked back into the living room and looked at her questioningly. She shook her head no.

"I suppose you were waiting for me to get home from school, so I could go get some, huh?"

Instead of answering, she turned and headed for her bedroom. I followed.

"Hey, what gives? What's the big deal about bread?"

She started to cry again. "Honey, we don't have any bread, and there's no money to buy any with."

"But didn't Dad get paid . . . . ?" Even before I finished the question, I had the feeling I knew the answer.

"Oh, Sherri, you know your father. He said he was feeling so bad about getting fired that he stopped in a bar on the way home and drank up most of his paycheck. He had a little left, and he bought that six-pack on the way home. Now we're absolutely broke."

"Broke? Don't you have even a dollar in your purse?"

She started to bawl again.

I hated the embarrassment at school, but the thought of going hungry absolutely terrified me.

"That's it!" I yelled. "I've had all I'm going to take of this nonsense. Mom, don't you realize what you just said? We're about to starve to death!"

"Honey, it's not quite that bad," she replied, wiping

her tears with her apron. "We do have a bag of potatoes. There's a little flour and milk. So we can have potatoes and gravy for supper. Tomorrow I'll go down to the welfare department, to see about some emergency funds."

"Welfare! Welfare! Welfare!" I screamed. "I can't stand it! I'll kill myself, before I have to suffer that embarrassment again! And I had my mouth all set for a peanut-butter-and-jam sandwich!"

I ran from the bedroom, out the back door, and into the yard. Frustrated and mad, I took it out on the garbage can. As I kicked, garbage went everywhere. Then I picked up the lid and flung it against the side of the house. It hit with a horrendous bang and clattered back toward me. I picked it up, gritted my teeth, and twisted my body around, like a discus thrower. The lid sailed down the driveway, out into the street, and then curved into a parked car. I didn't care. Even if they threw me in jail for disturbing the peace, so what? I'd had it with my family.

Just then, the neighbor across the street walked over toward the lid. "Hey, Sherri," he called. "Next time, try a Frisbee. It's not quite so dangerous!"

Talk about being embarrassed! Of all our neighbors to see my childish outrage, it had to be Mr. Haley. He was the kindest man on the block. His wife had brought us food so many times when Dad was out of a job, that I'd lost count. They kept trying to get us to go to their church with them. I did go to Sunday school a few times, when I was quite small. But Dad really didn't like to have anything to do with church, and I hated to get up early on Sunday and go with the Haleys.

Besides, from what I'd seen of Christians, their lives looked like Dullsville. I wanted to live—really live!

But right now, I was thinking how foolishly I had acted. I walked over, to get the lid back.

"What's the matter, Sherri?" Mr. Haley asked, as I took the lid from his outstretched hand. "I was out here weeding the flowers, and I heard a loud bang. I looked across the street just in time to see you wind up and let loose of that lid. It was headed straight for me. I offered a quick prayer, and it veered off and merely hit my car. Thank God you didn't knock my head off!"

He laughed, letting me know he wasn't angry. "Sherri, is there something I can do for you?"

I shook my head slowly and mumbled, "No."

He put one hand on my shoulder. With his other hand, he lifted up my head, to look into my eyes. "Sherri, I'm your friend. You can tell me, if you need anything."

I couldn't escape those eyes. They looked so gentle, so kind.

I wanted to blurt out the whole story: *My dad's an alcoholic and lost his job again. We have no money. We're being forced back on welfare.* It was so embarrassing . . . .

I started to explain it all, but nothing would come out. Then big tears trickled down and splashed off my cheeks. Mr. Haley gently put his arms around me and pulled me up to his chest. As I sobbed, how I wanted to tell him all about my deep hurts and pains.

He lovingly patted my shoulder. "There, there, Sherri. I think I know what happened at your house today. I've been outside working most of the day, and I saw your father come home. He's lost his job again, hasn't he? Well, Sherri, Mrs. Haley and I will do everything we can to help you. Most of all, God wants to make a real difference in your family. He can heal the hurts in your family and cure your dad of alcoholism. Jesus wants to bring real peace to your family. Oh, I wish you'd let Him do it.''

Could he be telling the truth? I glanced up and noticed his eyes brim with tears. Never before had I felt such compassion. I didn't even know it existed! Oh, if only my father had this kind of love for me, I knew my house would be a much better place to live in. But what Mr. Haley said was too much to even hope for. It would take a miracle to dry up an alcoholic like my dad, and I didn't believe in miracles.

I gently pushed myself away. "I'm sorry, Mr. Haley. I didn't mean to carry on like this. It's true that my father's drunk. He's lost his job again. I was so frustrated and mad that I went into orbit when Mom said we'd have to go back on welfare. We don't have any money at all!" I tried to keep back the tears this time, but no use.

Mr. Haley started patting my shoulder again. "Now, now, Sherri. Don't you worry, honey. I'm going to pray that things will turn out better. You know, I've seen the Lord work great miracles in so many people's lives, and I know the Lord wants to do the same thing in your family. It'll happen!"

Dreamer, I thought. *Miracles are like fairy tales.*

Or are they? Because just then, Mr. Haley pulled out his wallet. "Here's twenty dollars. Maybe this will tide you over."

I moved back from the outstretched bill. "Oh, no, Mr. Haley. I couldn't accept any money from you. I

mean—I mean, I didn't want to blurt out my problems.
I'm not looking for sympathy, or anything like that.
No, I just couldn't take any money from you.''

"Please take it, Sherri. I don't know how much you
believe in God, but this morning, God told me I would
find someone in need today and that I was to help
them. I believe God wants me to give this to you. It's
really an offering to the Lord, if you know what I
mean. I'd be so disappointed and hurt, if you didn't
take it.''

Was this man for real? Could a person actually hear
God speak? I guess I believed in God, but He seemed
like a hazy something, way off in the sky. Certainly He
didn't talk to people today, did He?

Before I could protest further, Mr. Haley grabbed
my hand, pushed the twenty-dollar bill into it, and
squeezed my hand shut. Then he wheeled around and
headed for his house.

I stood there, dumbfounded. When he got to his
porch, he turned and called, "God bless you." Then
he disappeared inside.

There I stood—with twenty dollars in one hand and
that stupid garbage-can lid in the other. I wanted to run
up to his house, ring the door bell, and give him the
money back. But maybe God did tell him to give it to
us. We sure could use it. Maybe God knew that, too. It
was kind of spooky.

I headed back to our house, to share the good news
with Mom. Then I thought of what we were going to
have for supper. It hit me: Why not give Mother the
surprise of her life? I'd hurry down to the store and
buy a big steak, to go with those potatoes and gravy!
She would say it was too expensive, if I asked her

about it. Yes, I'd get it and surprise her!

My exciting surprise took the sting out of picking up the garbage and getting it all back into the can. Then I carefully fitted the lid on the can and headed for the grocery store three blocks away.

At the back of the store was a long meat counter. All those packages looked so good. Oh, I loved good food. Then I checked the prices of the steaks. Wow!

I picked up one package. That wouldn't leave much from the twenty dollars! I put that one back and picked up another. It was a nice, thick steak, and it looked about right for the three of us. I could almost taste it. But it would take almost half of the twenty dollars . . . .

Then it hit me: *Why pay for it at all?* Stealing? Oh, I'd sneaked a package of gum or a candy bar now and then—and a package of cigarettes once—but a steak?

Why not? My family was hungry. Wouldn't that justify my actions?

No one was looking, so I quickly lifted my blouse and slid the package partway down into my jeans. I pulled the blouse over the top.

It felt awful, but my blouse fit really loose—no one could tell I had a steak hidden over my stomach.

So far so good, but Mom would want to know where I got it. If she knew I'd stolen it, she'd make me take it right back, so that's where the second part of the plan I quickly concocted came in. I headed for the candy counter and pulled a package of gum from the rack.

My heart beat wildly, as I walked up to the checkout counter. The clerk was busy with another lady, but he glanced at the front of my jeans. Oh, no! Could he tell? I wanted to bolt for the door, but my knees felt like jelly. I'd never make it.

The lady in front of me was taking an eternity to write a check. Why did these stupid women always wait until the clerk had completely rung up their groceries, before they even started to look for their checkbooks? Oh, that package felt absolutely horrible!

Then it began to dawn on me what I was doing. What would happen if I got caught? Would I go to jail?

That scared me so much, I decided to take the steak back to the meat counter. But a man behind me blocked the way. *Oh, what have I gotten myself into?*

Finally the lady finished writing her check, and I heard the clerk say, "Next."

I threw the twenty-dollar bill down and showed him the package of gum. "Anything else?" he asked, as he looked at me suspiciously.

He knows! I almost passed out on the spot!

"That'll be twenty cents," he said matter-of-factly. He turned to his register, punched some buttons, and counted out $19.80 in change.

I grabbed the money and headed for home. A block down the street, I got up enough courage to look back. Nobody was following me. I took off, running.

About a block from home, I pulled out the steak and looked at the price again: $9.25. Wow!

I still clutched the change tightly. Tucking the steak under my arm, I counted out $9.25 and slid that into my bra. Then I remembered the $.20 for the gum. I reached into my bra for the quarter and put a nickel back in. Then I hurried toward home, bounded up the steps, and kicked the front door open.

"Hey, Mom!" I yelled. "You're not going to believe this!"

She came out of the kitchen, wiping her hands on her apron. I walked right up and poked the thick steak into her arms. She looked at it unbelievingly.

"Sherri, where in the world did you get this? Oh, no! You didn't steal it, did you?"

I laughed. "Mom, for crying out loud. Don't you know your own daughter any better than that? I'm no thief!"

"Well, where did you get it, then? You don't have any money, do you?"

"Mom, you know Mr. Haley, across the street? I did a dumb thing, but it ended up well. He gave me twenty dollars, and I ran down to the store and bought this steak for supper. It was nine-twenty-five. And here's the change—ten dollars and seventy-five cents."

Mom was too flabbergasted at the whole turn of events to realize I had "spent" almost half the money.

"You mean Mr. Haley gave you money to buy this steak?"

"Not exactly, Mom. He gave me the money. I decided on the steak—to go with the potatoes and gravy. That Mr. Haley is a real Christian. He's helping us out. Isn't that great?"

"Sure is! I just can't believe the generosity of those people. I know they don't have much themselves, but they have always been so willing to help us out in the rough spots. I wish your father would let us go to church with them."

Mom brushed a tear away and walked back into the kitchen—with a $9.25 steak and $10.75 in change. And I had $9.05 in my bra!

"Well, honey," Mom called from the kitchen,

"things are looking up. I told you it wouldn't be so bad. Why don't you wash up and get ready for supper? I'll call your father."

I turned and smugly walked to my bedroom. It was a good thing Mom couldn't see the grin on my face. I didn't know stealing was so easy. I couldn't believe that I really had $9.05 of my very own—and steak for supper, too.

I flopped on my bed and chuckled quietly. I felt so proud of my accomplishment. Mom was cooking the steak. If she and Dad only knew it was already hot! That thought brought more chuckles.

Well, the steak was absolutely delicious. But the next day, I got the shock of my life. I discovered I wasn't the only thief in the family!

2

The following morning, when I got up for school, Mom had toast and cereal waiting.

"Hey, where'd you get the bread?"

She chuckled. At least she must be feeling better.

"After you'd gone to bed, I went down to that all-night store and bought some bread and milk and cereal. Oh, Sherri. Our good luck last night-just confirms the way I feel. Things are going to start working out for us. I just know it."

"Still going to go to the welfare department?" I asked.

She frowned. "Please, honey, let's not get started on that again. You know I have to go. When your father gets up, I'll send him out to look for another job. Something will turn up."

"Sure, sure," I said sarcastically. "Like it always does."

Mom didn't reply. She simply fixed herself a piece of toast and sat down at the table with me.

She was still there, idly nibbling on that toast, when I kissed her good-bye and headed for school. At least nobody there would know about our being on welfare—yet.

When I got home that afternoon, Mom was still sitting at the table. I knew she hadn't been there all day, but I could sense that something was troubling her.

But her troubles didn't satisfy my hunger pains. I said hello, opened the refrigerator, pulled out the bread and milk, and then got the peanut butter out of the cupboard. The jar was almost empty, but I scraped the sides, to get enough out for a sandwich. The peanut butter looked dry and chunky, but it tasted good. So did the milk.

I slid into a chair that was across the table from my mother.

"Sherri, there's something I must talk to you about," she began.

"Yeah, Mom. What's up?"

"Well, Sherri, it's just that . . . . What I mean is . . . . Oh, I'll come right to the point. The steak: Did you steal it?"

I almost choked on the sandwich in my mouth. Then I jumped up and yelled, "Steal it? Steal it? What do you think I am? I *bought* that steak. I gave you the change."

"Please. Please sit down," she said. "Let's discuss this calmly."

I eased back into the chair, eyeing her suspiciously.

"I was just asking, that's all," she went on. "When you came home, I noticed the steak wasn't in a bag and there wasn't any receipt. I guess I had a few wild thoughts, that's all."

"Okay, Mom, let *me* get right to the point. Look me right in the eye. Do you think I stole that steak?"

I tried to stare a hole in her. She couldn't take that, and she looked toward the wall.

I yelled it again: "Mom, do you think I stole that steak?"

"Of course I don't think you stole it."

"Mom, you're lying. I can't stand it when you don't trust me. Why don't we march right over to the

Haleys' house, and I'll prove to you that he gave me the money for that steak?''

''Well, honey, that's another thing. I ran into Mrs. Haley this morning. She didn't say one word about any twenty dollars. I mean, she didn't even mention it. I don't think she even knew that your father lost his job. So that made me think, *Where did Sherri get that twenty dollars? Where did she get that steak? Where was the receipt? Where was the bag?* You know, my mind began to build up all sorts of things.''

''Aw, Mom, you don't know the Haleys very well. I've heard, from some of the kids at their church, that they've got this funny thing about giving. Whenever they give something, they're not supposed to tell anybody. Maybe Mr. Haley doesn't even tell Mrs. Haley, when he gives someone money.''

''Oh, I see,'' Mom answered. Then silence.

''Sherri, what do you think about stealing? I mean, supposing someone were starving to death. Would you steal to give him something to eat?''

I smelled a rat on that question. I'd better be cagey. ''Well, Mom, what do you think? Would you steal, to feed someone who was hungry?''

''Of course I would!'' she responded without hesitation. ''But I'll tell you one thing. I'd never steal from poor people. I'd steal from the rich. They've got a lot, and they wouldn't miss it.''

''Well, Mom, that's exactly how I feel. I wouldn't mind ripping off the rich. They've got insurance.''

I knew she was up to something, but what? Had a neighbor seen me at the store and squealed? Maybe Mom didn't have the guts to call my bluff.

She sat there in silence for a few minutes and then

changed the subject. "I was down at the welfare department today. I don't have good news. They didn't give me any money."

"What?" I yelled. "Didn't you tell them Dad got canned and we're starving?"

"Of course I did. But how many times a day do you think those people hear stories like that? It's too bad for those of us who need help that there are so many people trying to rip off welfare."

"Okay for the sermon, Mom. But what are we going to do? Potatoes and gravy again tonight?"

She pushed back from the table, went to her room, and returned with her purse. She pulled out her wallet and spilled the contents on the table: six dollar bills and a little change. It came to $6.45, altogether.

"Sherri, with this, maybe we can get a little meat and some more bread and milk. I hope tomorrow the welfare department will have had time to study our case and come through."

"But, Mom," I protested, "six-forty-five isn't going to last very long. I know how much that steak cost. We'd better think of something!"

"Tell you what, Sherri. You go with me down to the store and help me look for some good buys. Maybe we can get enough food to last for a day or two, if we're really careful."

"You have to be kidding! That six-forty-five won't buy enough to keep a canary alive!"

"I know. So let's look on it as a challenge. Okay?"

Mom stuffed the money back into her wallet and the wallet into her purse. I really didn't want to go back to that store so soon, but I could tell she wasn't taking no for an answer. Did she have something else in mind?

Maybe that's why she brought up the subject of stealing!

Mom was uncharacteristically quiet, as we walked the three blocks to the store. I knew something must be bothering her. Was she simply worried about making the money stretch?

It was really pitiful, watching Mom at the meat counter. She'd pick up a package, look at the price, and sort of toss it back down. Then she'd pick up another and, with a look of despair, toss it down. She'd walk a few more steps, pick up some other packages, and toss them down. Poor soul. I knew she must be trying to find the best buy. But no matter what she selected, the price was going to be too high for our budget.

She motioned me over close to her and whispered, "Sherri, do you still believe in stealing from the rich to help the poor?"

"Aw, Mom, you wouldn't try anything like that in here, would you?"

"No. I guess not."

"Whew," I gasped. "I thought maybe you were going to knock off a few packages of meat."

"I've got a better idea," she told me. "It's safer. We're going to switch price tags on a meat package."

I jumped back. "Mom, you can't do that! That's dishonest! Besides, what would you do, if you got caught?"

"Oh, they'll never suspect me. I've shopped here for years. They'd never believe I'd do something like that."

"Mom, if you're going to do something like that, I'm heading for home now!"

Before I could carry out my threat, she grabbed my arm and whispered threateningly: "I know how you feel about stealing. You told me. I don't know how you got that steak last night, but I do know you stole it. Didn't you?"

So *this* was her trap! "Mom, how dare you say something like that?" I asked, in faked horror.

"Well, I can't prove it, but I'm sure you stole it. So you're going to help me with this. Now you do exactly as I say. Pull that label off that hot-dog package and hide it in your hand."

"No, Mom! Please!"

"Sherri, I'm not kidding. You and your father and I are going to starve to death, if I don't do something. That welfare check may not come for a week. I've got to stretch this six-forty-five as far as I can, but I can't buy meat and the other things we need. I love meat; you love meat; your father loves meat. And this is how we're going to get it. Now do as I say, or I'll slap you across the face, right here in front of everybody!"

Her eyes were raging. I knew she meant what she said.

I gingerly picked up a package of hot dogs and glanced around. I could see two people at the other end of the meat counter, but they were busy looking at prices. I snatched the label off the package of hot dogs and stuck it on my hand. Then Mom and I walked toward the roast she had spotted. She picked it up, held it against her stomach, and commanded, "Rip that label off and slap the hot-dog label on!"

I glanced furtively one way and then the other. Nobody was watching. I quickly exchanged the labels, and she tossed the roast into our grocery cart.

We were both too nervous to do much shopping, after that. She did pick up a loaf of bread and a quart of milk, and then she headed for the checkout counter. I noticed her nervously biting her lips. Had she done something like this before?

The clerk smiled at my mother. "Hello, Mrs. Lenier. How are you today?"

Mother just sort of grunted something and smiled back—weakly.

The woman rang up the milk. I held my breath. She rang up the bread. My heart beat wildly.

Then she took hold of the meat. She glanced at the price tag and instinctively punched the amount for the hot dogs on the cash register.

"That'll be two dollars and ninety-five cents, Mrs. Lenier," she said, as she stuffed the three items into a grocery sack.

We did it! We pulled off a heist!

With trembling hands, Mom tried to pull her wallet out of her purse. It dropped to the floor.

"What's the matter, Mrs. Lenier?" the clerk asked. "You seem sort of shaky and pale. Are you sick?"

"No, my mom's got arthritis," I responded. "She hates to admit it, but she can't hang on to anything very well."

"Oh, I'm so sorry," the clerk sympathized. "My mom has that, too. You should take aspirin, Mrs. Lenier. She says that really helps."

Mom had picked up her wallet but was still fumbling to get the money out. Finally she pulled out three dollar bills and held them out to the clerk.

"Let's see," the clerk said, "two dollars and . . . ." She looked puzzled. Then she reached over to the bag, pulled out the meat, and stared at it.

"Oh, my goodness. Something's drastically wrong here, Mrs. Lenier. This price can't be right."

She flipped the meat onto the scale—over three pounds.

"I'm terribly sorry, but there's been a mistake on this. This meat must have been marked wrong."

Mom and I exchanged worried glances. Now what?

"I'd better call the manager," the clerk said.

With that, I was ready to run for it. But Mom was in no condition to run. Besides, they knew her. Oh, no! My mother was about to be arrested for stealing. Now I would be known around school for having a drunk for a father and a thief for a mother!

Then something else hit me. I was the one who actually changed the labels! I'd be held as an accomplice!

When the manager came up, the clerk said, "Mr. Gilmore, this package of meat seems to be marked wrong. I wonder if those kids have been switching labels again."

"So that's it!" I blurted out. "I noticed some little kids monkeying around the meat counter. I bet those rascals were switching labels. I'll bet that was it!"

"Oh, for crying out loud," the manager said. "Those kids will be the death of me yet."

Mom chimed in. "You know, Mr. Gilmore, when I picked up that meat and looked at the price tag, I absolutely couldn't believe it. But you always have these fantastic buys here, so I didn't question the price."

Then she started to laugh. I did, too. I don't know if the clerk and the manager suspected anything, but at least they joined in our laughter.

Mom had lied her way out. Of course, I helped a little!

"Well, Mrs. Lenier, I'd love to sell you this meat for one dollar and fifty cents," the manager said, "but I imagine it will come closer to eight dollars."

"Eight dollars? Oh, I'm sorry," Mom responded. "That's too much money for me to spend on meat this week. My husband doesn't get paid until next week, so I guess I'd better look for something else."

"I'm sorry," Mr. Gilbert returned. "I wish meat weren't so high. I have to eat, like everybody else."

Mom quickly moved back to the meat counter. I grabbed the cart and followed. I didn't know what she'd do now.

She walked up to the hot dogs, grabbed a package, and started to cuss under her breath.

"Mom, please settle down. You're lucky they didn't nail you for that trick, so just stay cool."

Back at the checkout counter, Mom told the clerk, "Well, I guess it'll have to be hot dogs again. I guess they aren't so bad. I just wish I knew what they put in them."

She laughed nervously. The clerk didn't say anything—just took the money for the groceries—and we were on our way.

When we got home, Dad was there—sober. He sat at the kitchen table, munching on a piece of bread with nothing on it.

As I walked by him, I said sarcastically, "Dad, why don't you put something on that bread?"

He ignored me.

I repeated it. "Dad, you look silly, sitting there eating a piece of plain bread."

"Okay, Sherri. I'd just love to have some peanut butter or some jam on this. Or maybe some nice, yellow cheese and a little bit of green lettuce."

"Hey, Dad, you have a great imagination! Why don't you do something like that?"

He pulled the crust out of his mouth. "Sherri, take a good look at this bread. Of course I'd love to have some peanut butter, jam, cheese, lettuce, or whatever on it. But there's not a blessed thing in this house—only this dumb bread."

"Now, now," Mother interrupted. "I just bought some hot dogs at the grocery. I'll fry some potatoes. We'll make it."

At the supper table, Dad viciously bit into his food. I knew he was upset and didn't know how to express his feelings.

But I had my feelings, too. Would tomorrow bring the welfare check? If it didn't come, would Mom expect me to try to steal again? Was it going to be a way of life, from now on?

The hot dog on my plate reminded me of the whole mess at the grocery store. I felt so wretched and miserable that all of a sudden I got sick and pushed myself away from the table.

"Where are you going?" my dad demanded.

"I'm not hungry."

Without a word, he grabbed my half-eaten hot dog and stuffed it into his mouth. His manners reminded me of a pig!

Something had to happen around here—and soon!

3

I didn't take a lunch to school the next day. How could I sit in the lunchroom and eat two slices of white bread with absolutely nothing in between?

I usually ate with my friend Lillian. So later that afternoon, when we met in the hall between classes, she wanted to know, "Hey, Sherri, where were you at lunch today?"

"Aw, I just didn't feel like eating."

"Come on, Sherri. I've never known you to miss lunch—at least, not willingly. What's the matter? Nothing at home to fix your lunch with, today?"

I stared at her. Could she possibly know?

"Not that, Lillian. It's just that I finally started on that diet. I wasn't planning to say anything to anyone about it, you know. No big deal."

Lillian shrieked. "Sherri, you're not overweight. Come on. What's the real reason you weren't at lunch? You mad at me?"

"No! No!" I reassured her. "It's just like I said. I'm starting on that diet. That's all."

"Hey, Sherri baby, you can level with Lillian. My old lady said she saw your old lady in the welfare line yesterday. Your old man lose his job again? Drunk, huh?"

A chill ran down my spine. If Lillian knew, others knew. Soon it would be all over school. How humiliating!

"You better keep your mouth shut about that,

Lillian. It's not my fault."

"Hey, hey, come off it, friend. Welfare's not that bad. My family's survived on it. My mom and dad are on welfare; so are their folks. We've always been on welfare. Take it from me, kid—it's an easy way to go!"

"Well, it may be easy for you, but not for me. I'm just dying. I have some dignity, and . . . ."

"Hey, hey! " she cut in. "Don't you talk to me that way. I got my dignity, too. I get anything I want, and I've got plenty of it, too!"

"Sure, sure," I laughed, "you have everything you want. I know how far welfare checks go."

Lillian put her lips up by my ear. "Want to make some quick dough?"

I stared at her, as I pushed away. What was she getting at? Being a prostitute?

"Want to make some quick dough?" she repeated.

"So you think I've got a great body, huh? You said I didn't need to lose weight."

"Aw, get off it, Sherri. I'm not talking about selling your body. You wouldn't want to get into filthy stuff like that. Besides, prostitutes get full of VD, and probably some pervert would kill you. No way would I talk you into that kind of life!"

What was Lillian up to? I knew she always seemed to have money. If her folks were on welfare, how did she get it?

"Well, maybe I do need money—if you can get me some legitimately," I answered.

"What I have in mind is legit, Sherri."

I thought that rather strange. I'd never known Lillian to work. She usually hung around with a fast crowd after school. I knew she smoked pot. I'd even seen her high a few times at school.

"Okay, let me in on the big secret," I said.

Just then, the bell rang.

"No time now," she said. "You come to my house at eight tonight. I'll tell you then."

Something smelled fishy about Lillian's proposition, but I didn't really have time to think about it, and I did need money. So I told her, "Okay, see you at eight."

She smiled—but it was the wrong kind of smile. Somehow I just knew there was trouble ahead.

When I got home from school, Mom gave me the bad news: still no welfare check. She had to go back tomorrow.

At supper we ate the last of the hot dogs and bread. Mom, optimistic as always, said we had enough milk and cereal for the morning. That way, we could make it until she got the check.

I was concentrating more on Lillian and her suggestion than I was on the food. I just couldn't figure out what she was up to.

That evening I told my Mom I was going to Lillian's, to help her with her homework. Mom raised her eyebrows on that one. She was surprised I would help someone else; I seldom got my own finished!

Lillian lived two blocks away, in another dilapidated old house. A couple of abandoned cars rusted out in front. The house badly needed paint, and a corner of the porch looked as if it would collapse at any minute. Even before I got to the steps, I could hear the disco music blaring from inside. A mother dog and her eight puppies followed me to the door.

Lillian looked genuinely surprised when she answered my knock. "Hey, come on in, Sherri. Oh,

don't let those stupid dogs in." She gave the mother a
kick. "I really didn't think you'd come, but I guess
you're desperate, huh?"

"Let's not kid each other, Lillian. You know how it
is on welfare."

"After tonight, baby, you'll never be poor again!"
She laughed hollowly, then she ushered me into her
living room, where Maurice and Larry, two smart-
mouthed freshmen, sat. I'd heard both of them had
been in juvenile court. They both tried to act like big
men around school. I'd really wanted to smack them
across the head a few times, to teach them a few les-
sons about respecting a woman.

They were as surprised to see me as I was to see
them.

"Hey, Lillian," Maurice said, "you didn't say it
was Sherri you were inviting tonight. You sure she's
okay?"

"Yeah, Sherri's okay. I checked her out. She needs
the money, too. Don't you, Sherri?"

Half-embarrassed, I nodded. Then, with no further
explanation, Lillian guided us out the front door. I
couldn't make out where we were going—it was too
dark—and I didn't know if I should try to pry what we
were doing out of Lillian.

We must have walked a mile or so—over to a
wealthy, old neighborhood. The beautiful homes were
each set back on about two acres of land. A number of
them nestled up against a woods that grew along the
creek running through the area. I knew it quite well;
I'd been over here a few times, to admire the houses
and to play along the creek.

Maybe Lillian had a job, working for some of

these wealthy people at night?

As we walked along, Maurice and Larry would point out the houses without any lights on inside—some had just a porch light on. Finally, Larry said, "Let's try this one."

I whispered to Lillian, "What's going on? I've got a feeling you'd better fill me in—quick!"

"I can't right now, Sherri. Just tag along. Before this night is over, I bet you're going to be a hundred bucks richer!"

The four of us walked nonchalantly up to the front door, and Larry pushed the door bell. No response. He pushed the bell again.

Just then, the door opened, and a man stood there.

"Excuse me, sir, but is this where Yolanda Anderson lives?" Larry asked.

The man looked bewildered. "Yolanda Anderson?" he repeated. "No, no one by that name here."

What in the world was going on? I'd never heard of any Yolanda Anderson. She sure wasn't in school. Why would Larry be asking for her?

"Oh, excuse me, sir," Larry went on. "I must have the wrong address."

"What number were you looking for?" the man asked.

Larry fumbled in his pocket. "Just a minute. I have it on a piece of paper." He fumbled in his other pocket.

"What's the address here?" he asked the man.

"This is three-ninety-six Barrington Street."

"Oh," Larry responded. "I know it wasn't that street. We must have walked down the wrong way."

The man stood there, bewildered. I was even more bewildered.

"Sorry to have troubled you. Good night, sir."

"That's okay," the man answered. "Any time."

As we walked back to the street, I drew Lillian aside. "For crying out loud," I said, "what in the world is going on? I've never heard of Yolanda. She a friend of yours or theirs?"

"No, you dummy. That was just a come-on. We were checking to see if anyone was at home. Now don't ask any more questions."

We hurried to catch up with Maurice and Larry and walked with them a couple of more blocks, to another house with just the porch light on. By this time, it was about 9:30.

We walked up, as we had before, and Larry pushed the door bell. No answer. He pushed it again and again. Still no answer.

Larry turned and whispered, "Looks like a good one!"

We walked back to the street, and Larry started studying the curb. Was he looking for a cigarette butt?

He cursed. "Can't find one on this kind of street," he said. "I'll have to sneak up by the house."

As we stood in the street, Larry moved silently to the edge of the house, got down on his hands and knees, and began to paw the dirt around the shrubbery. I squinted and watched. Suddenly he stood erect and moved noiselessly back to us. "Okay," he said, "I got one. Let's walk on down the block."

Got one? One what? Why wouldn't they tell me?

Down the block, we edged into the woods, then doubled back, coming up right behind the house where we had just been—where no one had answered the door bell.

"Okay, everybody down and quiet," Maurice ordered.

He, Lillian, and I crouched. Larry walked a few feet ahead, wound up like a pitcher, and let loose of something.

Then I heard glass breaking. That had to be a rock he had thrown. That stupid Larry. What a dumb thing to do—break a window out here in the rich section of town!

Larry edged back toward where we were hiding. Just then, a light flipped on in the house.

"Quick! Move!" Larry ordered. We all took out after him through those woods, running as fast as we could. I tried my best to keep up.

When he figured we were safe, he stopped. That wasn't a moment too soon, as far as I was concerned.

Maurice spat on the ground in disgust. "I had a sneaking suspicion someone was in there," he said.

Between gasps for breath, I blurted out, "Come on, you guys, tell me what gives. First you ask for someone you don't know, then you break a window out of some rich guy's house. That is one of the most stupid ways to make money I've ever heard of. Don't you know you can go to jail for something like that?"

"Sherri, shut your mouth!" Lillian ordered. "We're not as dumb as you seem to think we are."

Maurice moved over next to me. "Come on, Lillian. Don't be so hard on her. She's new at this."

Then he turned to me. "Let me explain what we just did. We're checking these houses, to see if anyone's at

home. When we ring the front door bell, if they answer, we make up a name—like Yolanda Anderson.
But if they don't answer, that doesn't mean no one's
home. Some people are scared to answer their door at
night. But when we throw a rock through the window,
that scares the daylights out of them. Then they'll always flick on a light. That way we can tell they're
home. If no lights flick on, then no one's there. At least
we hope not."

So that was it. These three were robbing houses.

"I'd better head back home," I told them. "I'm not
up to something like this."

Lillian grabbed me by the shoulders and shook me.
"Hey, wait just a minute, little goody-goody. There's
nothing wrong with taking a few little items from these
rich people. They'll never miss them. Besides, they're
loaded with insurance, so it doesn't cost them a
dime."

"Yeah," I protested, "but you told me what you
had in mind was legitimate!"

"Legitimate? This is real legit. These people don't
know it, but in their own way, they're feeding the
poor. Maurice and Larry's folks are on welfare. My
folks are on welfare; so are yours. Nobody likes to be
on welfare, so we all need a few extra dollars in our
pockets, to lift our spirits. Let me tell you, Sherri,
when you walk around with a hundred bucks in your
pocket, it'll make you feel like a million!"

Lillian made it all seem so right. It sure wasn't any
fun, being on welfare. Besides, these rich people had
so much money, they didn't know what to do with it,
anyway. And those insurance companies were getting
richer by the day. I'd seen some of their huge buildings

in the city. It all sounded so reasonable. Nobody would miss a couple of little items.

"Okay," I responded, "count me in. But so help me, I hope we don't get caught. I sure don't want to go to jail."

None of them answered. I guess they were as scared of jail as I was.

By this time, we had walked out of the woods and down a couple of more blocks. Larry sized up another house. This time, when we walked up to the front door, my heart beat like crazy. I knew what we were up to now, and it scared the daylights out of me.

When no one answered the door bell, we returned to the street, found a rock, doubled around through the woods, and came up behind the house. This time, when Larry let loose of the rock and the window crashed, no light came on.

"Okay," Larry said. "Lillian, you stand guard. If someone comes, give two loud claps. Sherri, you stay next to me."

Half-crouched, Larry started for the house. I was right behind him, and Maurice followed. I ran to grab the back door, but just as I almost touched it, Maurice gave me a hard shove. "Sherri, don't ever touch a door! These doors usually have burglar alarms on them. As soon as they're opened, you'll hear a siren or a big clanging. Now don't be stupid!"

What could I say? I'd never studied breaking and entering. I didn't know about burglar alarms. We certainly didn't have any at our house. Of course, we didn't have anything worth stealing, either!

Maurice steered me over to where Larry was reach-

ing in through the broken window. Gingerly he undid
the latch and eased the window up—no alarm. Then
the three of us crawled in.

My heart was making enough noise to be a burglar
alarm! Supposing someone came now, with a loaded
shotgun, and blasted us!

Larry and Maurice headed for a bedroom, and I followed. They grabbed the mattress, flipped it, and
stripped off the sheets. Under the mattress they found
an envelope with about $20 in it.

"Stupid people!" Larry exclaimed. "The first place
you look for money is under the mattress. Then check
the closets—like inside the coats. Hey, Sherri, check
out that closet."

I did. Nothing there.

We had flicked on the lights in the bedroom, and
then Larry headed for the living room. He motioned
for me to follow.

"See that front door?" He pointed to it. "Look at
that lock system. That thing will go off, if you try to
break in."

He paused to wipe the sweat off his forehead, and I
realized it wasn't that hot. It must be nerves.

"I can never understand people," he went on.
"They put the best locks in the front and none in the
back. Burglars don't break in the front door; they
break in the back door or a back window. But these
stupid rich people put all the best locks on the front
door."

About that time, we both spotted a beautiful stereo
set. "Quick, grab that and go out. We'll meet you in
the woods. I want to check for guns."

When he said *guns*, I gasped. "Don't tell me we're

going to use guns to hold up people," I said. "I've never shot a gun in my life."

"Neither have I!" Larry laughed. "But they're hot items, and we can catch some quick money for them."

I could hardly manage the heavy stereo set by myself and staggered to the window. Lillian was standing there, so I pushed it out to her. She grabbed it and headed for the woods, while I climbed out. I went running after her, and in a few minutes, we heard Maurice and Larry close behind us.

When we had gotten far enough away from the house to rest, they showed us the two shotguns and the revolver they had found. "Great work, gang," Larry said.

We made our way across town by staying in the woods most of the way. When we had to leave the woods, we followed the alleys. After all, it's hard to look nonchalant, carrying a stereo set and guns in the middle of the night!

I kept wondering what we were going to do with the stuff. Larry had said we'd split everything evenly. It wasn't hard to figure out the $20. That would be $5 each. But what about the guns and the stereo set? I sure didn't want a gun. The stereo? Sure, I'd like to have it, but how would I explain that to my folks?

We were definitely back in the poor section of town now. Halfway through an alley, we stopped in back of a house. Maurice led the way into the yard and up to the back door and knocked. A man opened the door slightly. "Hey, who's this chick?" He pointed at me.

"That's Sherri. She's cool," Maurice answered.

The man opened the door all the way, and we walked in with the stereo and the guns.

"Hey, pretty good, kids. Pretty good," the man said admiringly.

"Well, what do you think, Willie?" Larry asked. "How much for all of it?"

The man looked the guns over carefully. I glanced around the room, as he did. It was a dilapidated old dump—dirty, junky. I wondered if he were on welfare, too.

Willie went to the window and peeked out around the curtain. "Anybody follow you here?"

"Come on, Willie; we're not amateurs," Maurice answered.

"Okay, kids. I'm in a generous mood tonight. I'll give you a hundred bucks for everything. No questions asked."

"Knock it off, Willie!" Larry yelled. "You take another look at those shotguns and that revolver. Study that stereo. That's a beautiful new Sony."

Willie dutifully studied the items again. "Yeah, I guess I was a little off. I'll make it one hundred and fifty dollars."

"Willie, you know better than that!" Larry countered. "That's good stuff, and you know it."

Willie looked as if he hadn't shaved in several days. He rubbed the stubble thoughtfully. "Okay, Larry. Two hundred bucks. But that's my final offer."

Now it was Lillian's turn. "Willie, you don't know what we had to go through to get this stuff. Two hundred bucks is only fifty bucks each. You know that stuff is valuable."

"Hey, wait a minute," Willie answered. "We're not talking about whether or not the stuff is valuable. But you've got to understand I'm a businessman. I buy wholesale and sell retail. I have to make something, to stay in business.''

I'd heard about guys like Willie before. Fences— that's what people call them. They buy stolen goods and resell them.

''Okay, I'll tell you what I'm going to do. You're nice kids, and I like doing business with you. So I'll give you three hundred bucks for the lot. That's seventy-five bucks each: not bad for a night's work. But I can't go any higher. Take it or leave it.''

I almost said, ''We'll take it.'' I'd be glad for seventy-five bucks. But I knew I'd better keep out of this.

''This stuff should bring us at least five hundred bucks,'' Larry said. ''But we'll settle for three hundred. Okay, gang?''

We all nodded, and Willie walked into another room and came back peeling off a wad of bills, giving each of us $75.

When he came to me, he said, ''Hey, kid, you're new at this, aren't you?''

That riled me. ''Okay, Willie, you can stop calling me *kid*. I just moved here from New York City. What you saw here tonight is just peanuts, as far as I'm concerned. I'm used to bigger things, but seventy-five bucks is seventy-five bucks.'' With that, I snatched the money out of his hand and stuffed it in my bra.

Inside, I was dying. Did he know I was bluffing?

When I got home that night, my parents were already in bed. I tiptoed in, but I tripped over Dad's shoe. Mom heard me and came flying out of her room. ''Sherri, is that you? Where in the world have you been?''

"I told you I was over at Lillian's house, helping her with an assignment, and . . . ."

"Don't you lie to me like that! I walked over there, and you were nowhere around!"

Oh, no! Now what was I going to say? I couldn't tell her we had just knocked off a rich man's house and sold the stuff to a fence.

"Okay, Mom, just settle down. When I was over at Lillian's, a couple of guys came by. They belong to the same church as Mr. Haley does. They said they were having a church youth party and invited us to come along. I didn't think you'd mind, since they were church kids. I guess I lost track of the time, though. Sorry."

Her frown gradually melted. "Well, next time you go off to some party, let me know. I've worried about you. It's not good for a young lady to wander around this town at night. Terrible things can happen. Don't you know that?"

"Yes, Mother, I know what can happen. I'm no baby."

I didn't wait for any more comments. I just headed for my room. She didn't follow, so I got ready for bed. I took the $5 Larry had given me and the $75 Willie had given me and folded them together. But where was I going to hide that money?

My first thought was to put it under the mattress. Then I remembered what Larry had said. No way was I going to hide money under a mattress!

Oh, well, I could worry about what to do with it tomorrow. At least I had $80. And Lillian was right: It sure did lift my spirits, to have that much money all my own.

But was it really mine? What if I got caught for what I had done tonight? Then what—reform school—jail?

I really should have thought about a place to put that money. If I had, maybe I wouldn't have run into that problem with the police, a couple of days later.

4

The next day at school, I got into a big hassle with Auggie, the wheeler-dealer of our junior class. He stopped me between classes and wanted to borrow $5.

"Five bucks?" I asked incredulously. "Auggie, you know my folks just went back on welfare. It's all around school. Where in the world do you think I'd get five bucks to lend you? Why, my old lady doesn't have enough money to buy groceries with!"

"Don't play games with me, Sherri. Everybody around school knows something else. They know you came into a lot of money last night. I heard that you, Lillian, Maurice, and Larry robbed a gas station."

"What?" I screamed. "That's a dirty lie! Who told you that?"

Auggie looked around. Then he whispered, "Michelle."

"Michelle?" I yelled again. He was trying to quiet me, but I paid no attention. "Auggie, you know Michelle as well as I do. You know she's a dirty, filthy liar. You can't even believe her when she tells you what time it is!"

"Okay, if you didn't rob a gas station, how did you get that money?" Auggie demanded.

"Well, to tell you the truth, we knocked off the First National Bank. We went in with these machine guns, tied up all the tellers, and got all their money. We went into their huge vault and carried out bags and bags of it. I'll bet we got at least five million, Auggie.

And you want just five dollars?''

"You're okay, kid," Auggie laughed. Then he leaned close and whispered, "Want to buy some grass?''

I should have known why he was hassling me. He was the biggest drug pusher in school.

"I got some good stuff just in," he continued. "Came from South America. I mean, this is quality stuff.''

Smoking marijuana wasn't my thing, but for some reason, I responded, "Sure. Why not?''

"How much you want?''

"Five joints.''

He reached inside his belt, pulled out five joints, and slipped them to me. "That'll be five bucks," he said.

I got the $5 out of my purse. I also pulled out my handkerchief, wrapped the joints in it, and slipped them down inside my pants, hoping they wouldn't fall out.

As I was walking home from school that day, I heard footsteps behind me. *Oh, no! The cops!* I sped up.

The footsteps sped up, too, so I turned to see if I should try to run for it. The cops must have smelled that marijuana I had!

But that's when I discovered Lillian, trying to catch up with me. "Where are you walking to so fast?'' she demanded.

"Oh, thank goodness, Lillian. I thought you were someone else.''

"Somebody else? You running scared after last night?''

"Yeah; last night still makes me nervous. I'm not used to this kind of thing.''

"That's what I wanted to talk to you about," Lillian continued, falling in stride beside me. "Have you heard the rumors going around school?"

"Yeah. Auggie was hassling me about it. I found out he heard it from Michelle. That's probably right, because she sure has a big mouth!"

"You can say that again. But I traced it down more than that. I'll bet you won't believe who opened their fat lips."

"Who?"

"Maurice and Larry!"

"Maurice and Larry!" I echoed. "You sure?"

"Positive! I ate lunch with Pauline. As soon as I sat down, she asked to borrow ten bucks. I said, 'What do you mean, ten bucks? I'm dead broke!' She laughed and said she knew I had eighty bucks. Well, when she said that, I knew something was up. So I said, 'Who told you that?' She said, 'Larry did.'

"Of course, I denied it, but she said she and Larry were in love, and Larry told her everything about the heist. Well, I suppose that stupid girl told somebody who told somebody who told Michelle. And now it's all over school."

What a fine mess! Now it wouldn't be long before some square kid would tell his parents; then they would call my folks—and that would be it.

I seethed on the inside. The absolute stupidity of that Larry! Didn't he know enough to keep his mouth shut?

Then I thought of those five joints I had bought. "Hey, Lillian, want to get high?"

"Why not? You got some stuff?"

"Yeah. I bought some from Auggie this afternoon."

We headed for the garage behind her house and lit up. Then we went into her house and played some wild disco music. But about 5:00, I decided I'd better go home. Mom might be looking for me. I sure hoped nobody had called her and told her what we had done.

I forced myself up the front steps, expecting the worst. As I stepped into the living room, Mom called, "Sherri! Come here!"

Oh, no! She knew!

But just then, she came bursting out of the kitchen, wiping her hands on her apron. "Sherri, Sherri! Wonderful news! I got the welfare check today. We're not going to starve!"

I breathed a sigh of relief. I'm sure she thought it was because of her news. It was really because of what she didn't know!

"And that's not all!" she went on excitedly. "Your father got another job. I just couldn't believe it, when he told me. He went down there this morning, and they hired him right away. It's in a warehouse, driving a forklift. I told the lady in the welfare department about it. She said we could keep this check, but this would be the end. It's enough to last us until your father gets paid."

"Oh, that's just great," I said—without much enthusiasm. I was still pretty nervous about our heist.

Well, I headed for my room. Before long, I heard Dad come home, whistling. That sure sounded good. But I knew it wouldn't be long before he was drunk again—probably when he got his first paycheck. Then he'd be drunk on the job and get fired. It was just like living in a revolving door!

I sat at supper that night without saying a word, just

picking at the good food Mother had prepared.

"Sherri," Mother started in, "I just can't understand why you are so unhappy. I thought for sure you'd be overjoyed to hear the good news."

"Aw, Mom, lay off, will you? I'm just not feeling too well. You know . . . ."

She nodded, looking a little embarrassed, and quickly changed the subject.

After supper I went to my room, to try to work on algebra. It seemed to have even less purpose now. I told myself that if I got out of the house for a while, I could clear my mind and study better. Mom and Dad were engrossed in a TV program, and I didn't see any point in disturbing them, so I sneaked out the back door and headed for the pizza place down the street.

When I was almost to the pizza place, I noticed a man standing in the shadows up ahead. He seemed to be watching me. My heart jumped into my throat. Was it a mugger? A rapist? A cop who knew about last night? I thought about running, but one foot just wouldn't move in front of the other. I learned what it is to be paralyzed with fear.

The shadowy figure moved closer and closer to me. He was within arm's reach now. Was he going to grab me? Something about him seemed familiar. Then it fit.

"Willie!" I exclaimed.

"I see you remembered me from last night. How you doing?"

"Okay now. But you scared me out of a year's growth!"

"Hey, hey, baby. That's no problem. You look great, just the way you are. I don't want you growing any more!" He looked me over approvingly.

I didn't know whether to be flattered or insulted.

"Now, wait a minute, Willie. If you think I'm that kind of a girl, you've . . . ."

"Naw," he interrupted. "I didn't mean nothing like that. I'm a fence, not a pimp!"

"Okay, but I get the feeling you were looking for me."

"Right, Sherri. I didn't know where you lived, but someone said it wasn't too far from Lillian's. I figured you'd probably get hungry for some pizza. This seemed like the most logical place to find you. I wanted to tell you that my customer really liked those guns. He wants some more. You going to go out tonight and do your thing?"

"Do what thing?"

"You know: bust into another house and get some more guns."

That didn't sound right. Stealing guns wasn't the right way to go in life. It might be nice to have a little money to carry around, but it sure wasn't any picnic, having to worry continually about getting caught!

"Listen, girl," Willie went on, "I got a lead on a house that is full of guns. If you get them, I'll give you top price."

"Willie, lay off it, will you? I was bluffing last night. I'm not really a professional burglar. I know very little about stealing, and I don't want to live that kind of life."

"Hey, baby, wait just a minute. I guess you didn't realize I was talking about big money. I mean really big money." He pulled out a wad of bills and started flashing it under the streetlight.

That just made me mad. He didn't have to take the

chances and go out and steal the stuff. All he was was
the go-between. I knew fences were hard to arrest. It
was stupid people, like me, who got busted.

He pressed me further. "I understand it's all over
school about you and Lillian."

"For crying out loud, Willie. How did you hear
that?"

"Oh, about an hour ago I ran into Maurice and
Larry. They were both high. They think it's a big
deal that everybody at school knows they're the big
men. I think it's absolutely ridiculous. If those two
smart alecks don't keep cool, someone's going to nail
them."

"Yeah, I heard that Larry is the one with the big
mouth. He told his girl friend, and she told a friend,
and now it's all over school. I'd like to get a gun and
blast that kid in the mouth. That would shut him up!"

Willie laughed. "Got a little spitfire in you, don't
you?"

"Well, I can't stand a rat."

"Now you're talking, baby," Willie went on sooth-
ingly. "That's just what I came to talk to you about."

"You mean knocking off Maurice and Larry? Oh,
no, Willie. You have it all wrong. I might steal from the
rich, but murder? No way!"

"Hang on, baby. I didn't mean anything like that.
I'm not into murder, either. I'm just a plain
businessman: I buy wholesale and sell retail. Mine's a
legitimate business. I get people what they want at a
good price."

What was Willie driving at? I had to know. "Okay,
Willie, what do you want with me?"

"You and me, Sherri, we're going to make some

big money. I know this house with these fancy guns, and I want you to get them. But first we have to understand a few things. I'm cutting off Maurice and Larry. They'll squeal under pressure. They can't keep their mouths shut. Besides, they're fast becoming junkies. A junkie would shoot his own mother for a bag of dope. I can't afford to have junkies working for me. You understand?''

Of course I understood. I'd read about junkies and knew a few from school. I promised him I'd never be a junkie—even if I did get a little high on marijuana that afternoon.

"Here's the address." Willie handed me a sheet of paper. "The guns are locked in a closet in the basement. I know the closet will be a cinch to break into. It has a lock on it, but this small crowbar will bust it loose. Use any method you want, to get into the house. It should be easy."

I held the paper so I could see the address in the dim light. "Hey, Willie, this is way across town. How am I going to get there? I don't have a car."

"No problem. I'll take you there myself."

"You mean you're going to drop me off in front of this house and expect me to break in and go into the basement and get these guns? Are you crazy?"

Willie laughed. "No! No! I don't expect you to do this by yourself. Why don't you take Lillian?"

"Lillian? Why Lillian?"

"Listen, kid, you better wise up. I know all about Lillian. I've bought stuff from her for a long time now. She's the slickest kid around, and she's never gotten caught. You're cagey, too, but you can learn a lot from Lillian."

Something within me said, *Sherri, run! Get away
from this mess just as fast as you can!*

Instead, I decided to explain to Willie why I couldn't
do it. "Listen, Willie, I just don't think I'm up to this.
It isn't right, and I'm scared to death of getting
caught."

"Not to worry!" Willie reassured me. "You pull off
this one tonight, and you'll be sitting so pretty that
you'll never have to pull another one. I don't know
how many guns this guy's got, but it's going to be
worth hundreds of dollars to you. Just pull this one;
don't ever pull another. That's simple, isn't it?"

He sounded so convincing. Then he pulled a bill
from the wad he had been flashing around, smoothed it
out, and handed it to me. It was a $100 bill. I'd never
seen one before—much less held one. It looked so big
and wonderful. Holding it in my hand gave me a sense
of power.

"Go ahead, kid; it's all yours."

"Mine? Why? I haven't done anything to deserve it!
What's the angle?"

"I'll bet you'd look gorgeous in some skintight
leather pants, a silk blouse, and some gorgeous
shoes," Willie observed, as he looked me over again.

He had me. All girls like clothes. It wasn't very
often that I got any new ones.

I looked down at the $100, then at Willie. As I did,
he pulled the bill out of my fingers. "Okay, I guess you
don't need clothes. Forget it."

"Hey, wait a minute!" I grabbed the bill back. "I
didn't say that!"

Willie broke into a wide grin. He knew he'd won.

"You're on," I told him. "But I want it understood

that this will be absolutely the last time for me. No way am I going to jail or reform school."

"Not to worry, baby. Old Willie'll take care of everything—even the cops. I have connections."

He led me to his car, and I was in for another surprise. "Hey, kid, you like it?" he asked.

"Like it? It's fantastic! Is it yours?"

"Yep, baby—all mine. And if you're a good little girl, I might even let you drive it, someday!"

That was a promise that never materialized, but no matter. For now, it was enough just to be riding in a Jaguar! I thought only rich people owned cars like that.

I wondered about Willie. Why did he live in such a run-down shack and yet drive a Jaguar? I asked him about it, as we drove toward Lillian's.

"Never judge a man by the house he lives in," Willie told me. "But I have a good reason. If I lived in a beautiful house and had fancy neighbors, when people like you and Lillian or Maurice and Larry came to bring me their goods, the neighbors would get suspicious. It wouldn't be too long until the neighbors would make it hot for me and call the cops."

So that was it.

"That's why I live in that old dump," he went on. "My neighbors couldn't care less what I do. Half of them are cheating the welfare department or ripping off somebody, so they're not going to turn me in. But I enjoy nice things, so I got this Jaguar."

We had pulled up in front of Lillian's house. I jumped out and went to get her. When she answered the door, I pointed toward Willie and the Jaguar. She knew whose it was.

"Sherri, whatever are you doing, touring around the town with Willie?"

"He just made a good deal with me, and I wanted to include you. But he's cut off Maurice and Larry. He knows they've been shooting off their mouths."

"Well, it's about time he cut them off. I never did trust those two characters."

As we drove toward the address, I told Lillian about the guns. Willie reached under the seat and pulled out the small crowbar. Lillian grabbed it and pushed it down the side of her jeans.

Willie let us out about three blocks from the address he had given me. "I'll wait here," he told us. "I can't risk being spotted too close to the house."

When he mentioned that, my heart skipped a beat. I didn't want to be spotted, either! As Lillian and I walked down the street, I got an idea. *Why not just take off and let Lillian do the job?* I didn't care if she got caught. Maybe she'd make more money, but at least I had the hundred bucks.

She must have been reading my mind. "How much do you know about Willie?" she asked.

"Nothing, really. All I know is what I got last night and this evening."

"Well, let me warn you of something. Willie's got quite a reputation. He'll never squeal on you, but you never want to cross him, either."

"What do you mean by that?"

"Let me tell you just one story, Sherri. One time Willie had a couple of girls working for him. He gave each of them one hundred dollars to do a special job for him. One of the girls took the money and ran off. Well, to this day, no one knows for sure what hap-

pened to her. But people say Willie found her and did
her in and buried her body in the woods someplace."

I gasped. What had I gotten myself into? In my
pocket right this minute was $100 I'd gotten from Wil-
lie. If I ran, or if I bungled this job, would he knock me
off and bury my body in the woods, too?

We were in the wealthiest part of town now, and I
checked the piece of paper again for the address.
These were big, beautiful homes, with lots of grass and
trees around them. We finally got to the address, and I
started down the long driveway.

"You sure this is the right place?" Lillian asked.

I looked at the paper and then at the house number.
"Yeah. The number's right.

"Sherri, do you know whose house this is?"

"Of course not. I've never been out here before in
my life. Do you know them?"

"Sherri, this is Judge Walker's house!"

"Judge Walker?" I yelled. "For crying out loud,
Lillian; no way am I going to bust into a judge's
house!"

"Shhh," she warned.

"No way am I going to bust into a judge's house," I
continued—in a whisper. "If we got caught, he'd
throw the book at us!"

I turned to walk away. Lillian grabbed my arm.

"Come now, Sherri. Suppose I told you that house
we busted into last night belongs to the chief of police?
What would you say to that?"

"Oh, no! No! The chief of police's house? Oh, Lillian, say it isn't so! We are in deep trouble!"

Then she laughed. "Naw, I was just kidding. I don't
know whose house it was. All I wanted to do was to

make a point. All houses are the same. Whether
they're doctors', lawyers', wealthy businessmen's,
police chiefs', or judges'—they're all the same.''

"Come on, Lillian, they're *not* all the same. Can you
imagine what would happen if we got caught stealing
here? The judge would have no mercy!''

"Big deal!'' Lillian sneered. "Now come on. We
have work to do.''

The house was dark. Only the porch light glowed,
giving a kind of eerie feeling to the long driveway.

I thought I would pass out before we ever got up to
the front door. Maybe I should have passed out. It
might have saved me a lifetime of hell!

5

A wide expanse of lawn, shrubs, and large trees separated the house from the road, and I don't think anyone could see us, as we walked up the long driveway. Apparently the judge liked privacy—and that was working to our advantage, at the moment.

But the closer we got to the house, the harder my heart beat. In the distance, I heard a dog bark. "You think the judge keeps police dogs around, Lillian?" I asked, trying not to let my terror show in my voice.

"Well, I hope not, Sherri. Maybe this judge is smart and doesn't keep police dogs."

"What do you mean, smart?"

"Well, things are changing. I heard about a guy who had two police dogs. He was at work, and his four-year-old girl let the dogs out. A doctor just happened to be jogging down the road, and those dumb dogs thought he was a burglar. They leaped on him, knocked him down, and started to rip him apart. Just then, the owner came home. He jumped out of his car and called off the dogs. The doctor was rushed to the hospital, where he finally recovered."

"Oh, no, Lillian. You don't think something like that is going to happen to us, do you?"

Lillian chuckled. "Well, it might not be so bad. The doctor sued for two hundred thousand dollars and won! So if you and I were attacked by the judge's police dogs, we could claim we were just out here jogging, and sue him. Each of us could end up with two

61

hundred thousand dollars!''

Big deal. I could visualize myself screaming, while vicious, snarling police dogs gouged the flesh from my face and ripped the meat from my bones. *Some things are more important than money,* I decided.

''I guess police dogs aren't as bad as Doberman pinschers,'' Lillian continued. ''If those big brutes attack you, they bite so hard they can break your bones—just snap them right in two, like that!'' She snapped her fingers.

''Hey, knock it off, will you?'' I countered. ''I'm scared enough, as it is. You're not making it one bit easier, with these dog stories. So help me, Lillian, if I hear a dog bark in this yard, I'm taking off!''

She didn't say any more. She knew I was a novice and that we both had to be alert, to carry out this heist. It wasn't helping anything, to make me more nervous.

When we finally got to the front door, Lillian rang the bell. No answer. She pushed the door bell again. That's when I heard the dog bark—right behind me.

I did what I had said I'd do: I flew off those front steps and headed for the woods. Then the dog barked again, and it sounded as if it was ahead of me, so I made a quick turn and headed back for the porch. Somehow I knew I'd be safer with Lillian.

As I ran, I could almost feel that dog leap onto my back and sink its teeth into the back of my neck.

I made it back to the front steps, threw my arms around Lillian, and panted, ''What are we going to do?''

''Oh, for crying out loud, Sherri. Will you stop it? Turn around. Look what's chasing you.''

Frightened out of my wits, I hesitatingly turned.

There at the bottom of the steps stood a little, white toy poodle, happily wagging its tail and yapping.

Lillian bent down, and the little poodle ran up the steps and jumped into her arms and began to lick her face. "Oh, isn't she cute?" Lillian asked.

"Whew!" I laughed nervously. "That sure fooled me."

But as I reached over to pat the poodle, a huge—and I do mean huge—black dog edged around the corner of the house and growled. Lillian and I both froze. *This* one meant business!

Just then the poodle wiggled out of Lillian's arms and ran toward the huge black dog. Would you believe that big dog started to wag his tail? We were saved by a poodle!

The poodle took off toward the woods, with the big dog romping along after her.

"Come on, Sherri," Lillian said. "Those dogs probably belong to a neighbor. I don't think anybody's at home here. Maybe the judge has night court."

I was still shaking from my encounter with the dogs, and I was ready to call it quits. But then I remembered the hundred bucks—and Willie. I wanted to live! "Okay," I said, "let's grab a rock. We'll circle around and throw the rock through a window."

"Hey, you catch on quick," Lillian responded. "One job, and you sound like a pro!"

Her comments sort of pleased me—anybody likes compliments. But they almost made me nervous. I remembered what I had told Willie—this would be absolutely the last time.

We moved cautiously through the woods, toward the back of the house, trying not to get those dogs following us. We kept whispering instructions and comments, to keep in touch.

Then something hit me. How did Willie know right where the guns would be? I asked Lillian about it.

She chuckled. "Willie's got lots of friends, Sherri. I hear tell he's paying off a TV repairman. Oh, the man is legit—he does repair TV sets. But he also cases the houses while he's inside. He tells Willie what the people have and where it is. Probably he cased this house for Willie. Maybe the judge even showed the TV repairman his guns. People get pretty stupid sometimes, but they're so proud of their possessions that they show them off to total strangers."

By this time we had emerged from the woods at the rear of the house. I realized that the rock in my hand seemed awfully small. I never was very accurate at throwing things. I just hoped I'd be able to hit the window.

I cocked my arm to throw. But just as I did, Lillian whispered, "Stop, Sherri! Don't throw it!"

"What's the matter?"

"I smell something fishy."

Well, when she said that, my heart went into orbit! I trusted Lillian's experience in stealing.

"Now what?" I asked. "Think we'd better get out of here?"

"Not yet. I just got to thinking that if that judge has a lot of guns in there, he probably had his house wired, too. We'd better check, before you throw that rock. He may have his back windows wired, so that if a glass breaks, it sets off an alarm. You know—the kind of setup they have in a jewelry store. Sometimes these things even have wires that lead down to the police station. A judge is very likely to have that kind of system.''

"Listen, Lillian, I feel it, too. Something's wrong with this whole deal. I just don't think we ought to go through with it.''

"Well, let's not give up yet. Just let me check out one thing. I'll be right back. You wait here.''

I crouched at the edge of the woods, while Lillian crawled to the back of the house. I could barely see her as she ran her hand alongside the windows. Then in a few minutes she crawled back to where I was waiting.

"Just like I thought,'' she announced. "That stinking judge has his windows wired. If you tossed that rock, you would have heard a sound you would never have forgotten!''

I could see it all now: being busted for breaking the judge's window—my fingerprints all over the house!

"Let's get out of here, Lillian, and forget the whole deal. Willie will understand.''

"Naw; we've come this far. Besides, I like a challenge. I have another idea. Come on, follow me.''

Once again she crept toward the back of the house. This time, I followed, half expecting to see the judge come flying out the back door any minute, to blast us to smithereens. And I kept glancing around for the vicious black dog. I really don't know when I've ever been so frightened.

When we got to the back door, Lillian pulled out the crowbar. "Okay,'' she said, "I'm going to take one big chance.''

"What in the world are you going to do?''

"I'm going to take this crowbar and push it between the door and the lock. I'll dig out the wood and push back the bolt. When that bolt comes back and I slowly open the door, if you hear an alarm, run for your life!''

"Wait a minute! Wait just a minute!" I protested. "Maurice almost clobbered me last night for touching the back door. I may not know as much about these things as you do, but common sense says that if a guy has his windows wired, he is going to have his back door wired."

"Cut it out, Sherri. I know what I'm doing."

That made me mad. "Okay, Miss Smarty, so you know what you're doing. But remember this. I was the one who asked you to come along. I'm telling you right now, Lillian, if you open that door, the alarms are going to go off!"

All this time, she kept chipping away at the door. As she worked, she retorted, "You shut your mouth, stupid. I know a lot more about alarm systems than you do. Usually the alarms for windows are on a separate system. Nine times out of ten, when people leave by the back door, they forget to set the alarm."

She kept chipping away at the frame. I kept my ear against the door, listening for any sounds of life inside. Then I thought, *Suppose the judge shoots through the door?* I'd seen that in the movies, so I quickly moved to one side. If he blasted through that door, he was going to hit Lillian, not me!

"Okay, I got the bolt exposed," she said. "Now I'm going to push it open slowly. You get ready to run!"

I backed away and faced the woods. She wasn't going to have to worry about me not running fast enough!

My curiosity aroused, I turned toward Lillian again, just in time to see her push the bolt back very delicately. Then she reached for the door handle and pushed gently. I held my breath. My leg muscles tensed, as I got ready to run at the slightest sound.

The door came open. Not a sound!

I glanced at Lillian. She looked back and grinned, as if to say, "I told you so!"

When we stepped inside, Lillian shouted, "Hello! Anybody home? We need help!"

Well, when she yelled, I almost jumped a foot off the ground!

"Lillian, what in the world are you doing?"

She chuckled. "You didn't want me to tell them I was a burglar, did you? You always say, 'I need help.' Then if someone is in the house, at least they won't shoot you first and ask questions later."

We stood there a minute, as our eyes became accustomed to the darkness of the house. The silence was eerie! I could hear a grandfather clock ticking somewhere.

We crossed the kitchen and tried several doors, before we found the one leading to the basement. Lillian flicked on the light.

The steps led to a beautiful recreation room—pool table, TV set, stereo. I saw Lillian glance at the stereo. "Remember," I told her, "only guns. And let's get out of here quickly, before something happens."

She spotted the cabinet against the wall. Just as Willie had said, it had a lock on the outside.

"This must be it," she said quietly.

She took her crowbar, pushed down hard, and jerked back. The lock came off as if it had been put on with tape.

She jerked open the door, and there stood four very

expensive, high-powered rifles and three beautiful revolvers. They must have been collector's items. And there were boxes and boxes of ammunition! What an arsenal!

Lillian grabbed a revolver and threw it into my hands. "Push it down the front of your jeans," she ordered. "No, not all the way. Let the handle hang out, like this." She showed me, as she tucked one into her jeans, then the other.

"Grab some bullets, Sherri," she said, as she stuffed some into her pockets.

"Willie didn't say anything about ammunition," I protested.

"I know. I know. But we need them, just in case we have to blast our way out of here!"

"No, Lillian! No! No! Not that! I mean, we're not going to get involved in a shoot-out!"

"Shut up and do what I tell you, Sherri. If we're surrounded, there's no way they're going to take me alive. I'm not about to go to jail."

"For crying out loud, Lillian, don't talk that way! If I knew it involved all this, I never would have come tonight!"

"Listen, kid, you're into this just as much as I am. Now if somebody comes, at least we'll have guns to fight them with!"

I still hadn't taken any bullets, so she started to stuff some into my pockets.

"Lillian, this is absolutely crazy. I don't even know how to load a gun, much less shoot one!"

"Shut up and quit being a baby," she ordered. She threw two of the rifles into my arms. "Now take off!" she told me, as she grabbed the other two rifles.

As I started up the steps, the bullets dropped farther into my pocket. As they did, I thought of that $100 bill down there. All of a sudden, it seemed absolutely worthless. For a lousy $100, I was putting my life on the line. I told myself that I would never again be this stupid!

We ran out the back door and into the woods. It was no small task, trying to run with those heavy guns, tripping over dead trees and stumps, getting slapped in the face by overhead branches. Finally I felt I couldn't go another step. "Lillian, let's stop. I'm about to collapse."

"Shut up and keep running," she called back. "The farther we get from that house, the better off we'll be!"

I gritted my teeth and kept going. My legs felt like Jell-O, but I kept pushing harder. I could taste the blood coming up in my mouth. Just when I thought I couldn't possibly take another step, we cleared the woods and stood at the edge of a road. But before I had a chance to catch my breath, a car turned a corner and headed toward us.

"Quick! Jump back into the woods and lie flat!" Lillian ordered.

She didn't have to tell me twice! When I lifted my head just a little, to see what was happening, I noticed her jamming a bullet into a rifle.

"Oh, God, what have I gotten into?" I whispered. "Please get me out of this mess."

"Shut up, will you?" Lillian commanded. "God's not about to help you pull off a burglary, you stupid nut!"

The car slowed, as it approached where we were hiding.

"You don't suppose he saw us, do you, Lillian?"

"I don't know, Sherri. But if he stops, I'm going to blast away first and ask questions later!"

"No! No! Please, Lillian! Don't do anything so stupid! I'm not about to be an accessory to a murder!"

"Shut up, Sherri, or I might just turn this gun on you and blast your pretty face to smithereens!"

I couldn't believe what was happening. It seemed like a horror movie or a nightmare in slow motion.

I never was one to pray, but I prayed—silently, this time. I told God that if He got me out of this mess, I would never steal again. It felt strange—praying to Someone I wasn't even sure was there. I kept my eyes glued on that car. "Oh, God, please don't let it stop!"

Just as he got about where we were, he slowed even more and started to pull to the side. Lillian aimed in his direction. I gritted my teeth. This was the end!

But he drove by!

I raised my head a little and then pushed out of the woods, still flat on my stomach. A way down the road, he turned in at a driveway.

"Oh, no!" Lillian exclaimed. "That must have been the judge. He turned in at the house we just came out of!"

I leaped up. "We'd better get out of here quick—just in case he saw us!"

"Right you are. Back through the woods, Sherri! The cops will be here any minute now!"

We both grabbed our arsenal and took off. I was so exhausted from the previous running that I thought for sure my lungs would burst. But I knew that now I really was running for my life!

Twisting, tripping, falling, stumbling, we finally got
to another side of the woods, farther away from the
judge's house.

Out of breath, Lillian turned to me and said, "We
have to stash these guns. We can't walk up to Willie's
car with guns in our arms. Bring all your guns over
here. We'll hide them under this bush."

We pushed the rifles and the revolvers under the
bush, and Lillian kicked some leaves over them. Then
we stepped out onto the road.

"Okay, now we have to remember where they are,"
Lillian said. "Take a good look around. Study the
area. Here, let me make a mark with my foot in the
gravel at the edge of the road."

As she was doing that, she went on, "Okay, that
bush is next to this trench, and this trench is next to
this big tree. How far do you think we're away from
that house?" She pointed.

I had no idea how far it was.

"Let me see," she went on. "Looks like about two
hundred feet to that driveway. That right, Sherri?"

I was so confused and exhausted and scared to death
that I couldn't have told the difference between two
hundred feet and two hundred inches! But I blurted
out, "Yeah, about two hundred feet."

"Okay, Sherri, let's find Willie."

She no sooner had the words out than another car
turned the corner and headed toward us. Instinctively,
we both dove into the woods.

I wasn't quite as nervous, this time. If this car
stopped, at least Lillian didn't have the gun, so there
wouldn't be some poor, unsuspecting guy getting his
head blown off!

Then I noticed Lillian slowly edging her way back to where we had hidden the guns. Oh, no!

Fortunately this car didn't even slow down when it went by. I breathed a huge sigh of relief.

We crawled out from the woods, started down the road, turned a corner, and then, up ahead, I saw Willie's Jaguar. I don't know when I was ever so glad to see someone!

I passed under a streetlight as I hurried toward his car. That was when I noticed my blouse was torn. Blood was coming from a deep scratch on my arm. I must have looked terrible.

Willie got out to open the door for us. "My goodness, you girls look like you tangled with some lions!" he exclaimed. "What happened? Did it go wrong?"

"No, everything went perfectly," Lillian answered as she climbed in. "I mean just perfect. We got four gorgeous, high-powered rifles and three beautiful revolvers. Willie, you're going to love us forever!"

Willie threw his arms around me and hugged me. "I just knew you had it in you, kid. I'm really proud of you!"

"Willie, cut the mush!" Lillian called. "We aren't home yet! We stashed the guns. Let's go get them."

By this time, I was in the Jaguar. Willie ran around and jumped in. The tires spun in the gravel, as we took off.

"It's over three blocks and to the right," Lillian said.

Just then, a siren screamed behind us. I threw myself to the floor.

"Get up here—quick!" Willie ordered. "Act as if nothing happened!"

He jerked me by the hair, as he said it. I sat there

trembling. But the police car sailed right on by us, with sirens wailing.

"Everybody just stay cool," Willie said. "The cops won't stop a Jaguar in this area. They know it belongs to some rich dude. But I still think we'd better cool it."

He made a quick U-turn and headed back to his house.

"You girls look terrible," he said, when we got inside. "You'd better wash up and comb your hair."

Lillian and I made our way to his bathroom. It was absolutely filthy. I hated to use the only washcloth there. I bet it hadn't been washed in a year!

I got my hands clean and then washed the blood off my arm and tried to straighten my hair. I discovered I even had some scratches on my face, but a little makeup covered them.

"Lillian, what are we going to do now?" I asked.

"Oh, we'll probably stay here a few hours."

"What do you mean, a few hours? I have to get home! My old lady will be worried about me."

"Aw, come on, Sherri. Your old man and old lady don't care that much about you, do they? Mine don't."

I wondered. *Did my folks really care what happened to me? How would they take it, if I got busted for stealing? Did they love me?* I know I didn't feel any love.

"Besides, Sherri," Lillian went on, "think of all the money we made tonight!"

"What do you mean? We haven't got a dime! Here we stand, all bruised and battered and torn, and those guns are out there under some dumb bush. Who knows? Maybe the cops have spotted them already and picked them up."

"Not on your life. We hid them too well."

I wasn't so sure about that.

We had pulled ourselves together as best we could, under the circumstances, and we went out to Willie's living room. He had the TV on and was watching the late movie, so we joined him. Later he went out and got some pizza. He also came back with some pot. I decided to try it again; after all, I really needed something to calm my nerves. As I inhaled it, I began to feel giddy. Things weren't so bad, after all.

The movie was boring, and I must have fallen asleep, for the next thing I remember, Willie was nudging me. "Okay, wake up, sweetheart. Let's go get those guns."

It wasn't much fun driving across town this time. The closer we got to where the guns were stashed, the more scared I became. Somehow I just knew the cops would be there, waiting for us!

6

Lillian remembered right where we had stashed the four rifles and three revolvers. "They're just up ahead, by that bush, Willie," she said. "Hit the brakes. We'll fly out of the car and grab them, and then we can take off."

I held my breath. Were the guns still there? At least I didn't see any cops around.

As soon as we got alongside the bush, Willie slammed on his brakes. We flew out of the car and dove into the bushes. Lillian quickly brushed away the leaves. Yep—still there! She grabbed the rifles and shoved them into my arms. "Take those to the car and hop in. I'll be right behind you."

As I got the rifles loaded into the car, I heard her in the bushes, cussing. I started back toward her, when suddenly she started for the car. "I thought I told you to get in the car," she said menacingly. "Now get in."

I obeyed. "Here's two of the revolvers," she said. "I still can't find the third one." With that, she dove back into the bushes again.

Car lights were heading our way. "Lillian!" I called, "hurry! Someone's coming!"

"Get out of here! Get out of here!" she called back. "I'll hide here and find that revolver. We've had too much risk, getting this far. I'm not giving up!"

My door was still half-open when Willie took off, heading toward the oncoming car.

Somehow I managed to get the door closed and hang

75

on to the seat. But as we got close to the car, Willie slowed down. That's when it happened. The red lights on the car came on, and it started to pull in front of us.

Willie jammed the accelerator to the floor, hit the shoulder, and tore out of there. The cops U-turned and were hot on our trail.

Willie knew how to make that Jaguar move, but I shrieked in terror when I saw a sharp curve ahead.

"Hang on!" he yelled.

The car started to skid. Willie raised up off his seat, wildly fighting the wheel. I don't know how he did it, but he pulled that baby around that curve. That was some driving!

I guess the cops knew they couldn't make that curve and had to slow down. Anyway, Willie made a couple of quick turns. I looked back and saw the police car go barreling by, straight ahead. Willie had tricked them!

"Whew!" he said. "I guess maybe we're safe now."

Safe! Then I thought of poor Lillian, still stranded back there under that bush. "Let's go get Lillian," I said.

"No! No," Willie responded, "too risky!"

"What do you mean, too risky?" I yelled. "You're not going to leave her stranded, are you? How could you be so heartless?"

"Now, Sherri, just calm down. Lillian's a smart gal. As soon as she saw those red lights, I know she headed deep into the woods. Even if we went back, we wouldn't find her where we left her. Furthermore, those cops aren't dumb. You'd better believe they're heading back in that direction right now. They're wondering what's under that bush."

"You think they'll find that revolver?"

Willie chuckled. "Knowing Lillian, she's already running through the woods with that revolver tucked in her jeans!"

Willie took an indirect route back to his house—just in case. When we pulled up there, I wondered how we were going to carry in that arsenal.

Willie must have thought of that, too.

"Dumb me!" he said, and we took off.

About four blocks away, we stopped. "Just stay right here," he told me. "I'll be right back."

He went up and pushed the door bell. *Don't tell me he was planning to knock off a house in this neighborhood?*

He pushed the door bell a couple of more times. Finally a light came on and a man in a bathrobe opened the door. He stuck out his hand toward Willie, and the two shook. Then Willie followed the man into the house.

A few minutes later, Willie reappeared, carrying one of those cases musicians who play the bass use. Willie wedged the case into the backseat, and we took off for his house again. But on the way, he pulled into a dark alley. He reached around and opened the case. I turned to see what he was up to, then I noticed the case was empty. Willie carefully placed the rifles in the case and locked the lid.

I felt so stupid. Why couldn't I have figured out something so obvious? I guess I just didn't have a criminal mind.

Willie pulled out of the alley and drove back to his house. We marched right in the front door, Willie carrying the bass case and me with the two revolvers tucked in my jeans.

Once inside the living room, Willie pulled out the guns and lovingly fingered them, twisting, turning, checking every part. "Beautiful! Absolutely beautiful!" he said.

Just then, we heard a car stop out front. Willie grabbed the guns, stuffed them into the case, and pushed the whole thing behind the sofa.

Someone knocked on the door, and Willie carefully opened it a slit. Then he threw it open and laughed. "It's about time! What took you so long?"

There stood Lillian—with that revolver in her hand. I thought it was rather stupid, carrying the gun like that.

"Man, we just got here, ourselves," Willie said. "How did you get here so fast?"

"Simple; very simple!" Lillian said proudly. "I just used the oldest profession in the world."

I knew what that meant—prostitution. "You want to run that through again?" I asked.

"Well, it was quite simple," Lillian explained. "After I saw the cops chase you guys, I knew I only had a few minutes to find that revolver. I knew they'd be coming back, so I couldn't take too long. Well, I rummaged around and found the gun, tucked it in my jeans, and took off. I came out on the other side of the woods, in a residential area.

"As luck would have it, I saw a couple coming out of their house. As they walked toward their car, I came up—sobbing up a storm. They asked what was the matter, and I told them I had to go looking for my father, and I thought he was down at a certain bar. Then I asked if they would mind driving me down there, so I could bring my drunken father home. I told them my mother was at home, bawling her eyes out, too, and I was sorry to cause them so much trouble. And would you believe those dumb people thought I was telling the truth?''

That was Lillian. She was as good at making up stories as I was—so believable.

"They let me out at the bar," she continued, "and I went inside. It was mostly men in there. I sidled up to one who wasn't all the way out and smiled. I put my arm around him and purred, 'Would you like to take me home?' ''

Lillian laughed, relishing her cleverness. "I just wish you could have seen that guy. He came flying off that bar stool!

"He put his arm around me and led me out to his car. I gave him directions here. Well, when we pulled up out front, he decided he wasn't going to wait any longer.

"That's when I jammed this revolver in his ribs and said, 'Mister, don't get any wild ideas. I'll call the cops and have you arrested for molesting a minor. They could put you away for ten years for getting involved with a teenager like me!' ''

Lillian laughed again. "You should have seen him back away from that gun. I'm sure he thought about his wife and kids at home. I hardly got out of that car before he was burning rubber to get away. Well, here I am, and there's the gun." She slipped it into Willie's outstretched hand.

"Lillian, you ought to go into the fencing business," Willie said admiringly. "You have an idea for everything. I bet you could make a bundle."

We all laughed.

Willie laid the revolver on the floor, pulled out the bass-viol case, and arranged the other guns on the floor, too. Then he headed for his bedroom and came back flashing that wad of money. "Okay, girls, here's the deal. I'm going to give you a thousand bucks for this haul. Five hundred each!"

I couldn't believe it. Five hundred dollars. *Oh, was that in addition to the one hundred dollars I already had, or . . . .*

Willie must have read my thoughts. "Sherri, that other hundred I gave you earlier—that's a bonus. I'll give Lillian an extra hundred, too. That way you'll each be making six hundred bucks for one little night's work. Not bad, huh?"

I glanced toward Lillian, and we both nodded approval.

Willie gave us our money in twenties. Did I ever feel rich, when I wadded it up and stuck it in my pocket!

"It's so late," Willie said, "I'd better drive you both home." But when we pulled up in front of my house, the lights were still on. I couldn't imagine my folks still being up. Maybe they really were worried about me.

But any thoughts like that melted, as I walked up to the front steps and heard angry voices coming from inside.

I shoved the front door open, and there stood my mother and father. Dad was drunk again.

They both turned when I entered, and now I became the object of Mother's wrath. "Young lady, where have you been?" she demanded. "Don't you know what time it is? It's four in the morning!"

"Now, Mom, just cool it," I responded. "I was home earlier—I came in the back door. You were watching TV. I guess you didn't hear me. Anyway, I went right to bed. When you two started arguing, it woke me up, and I couldn't get back to sleep, so I slipped out for a breath of fresh air. Don't you know that I just can't stand you two fighting and arguing all the time?''

With that, I faked a good cry. Then I mumbled, ''And here I come back, and you're still fighting. Then you tear into me, too. I don't know what I'm going to do. I guess I might as well run away from home or go jump off a bridge.''

I bawled some more—doing an awfully good job of faking it, if I do say so myself. Mom came over and put her arm around me. ''Now, now, honey, please don't take it so hard. I have my troubles with your father.''

At that, Dad staggered toward me. ''Honey, you must understand I only had a couple of beers. I just needed a little something to help me relax, that's all. It's just that your mother gets all uptight whenever I touch one teensy little drop.'' With that, he fell into a nearby chair.

I didn't say anything else—just headed for my bedroom. Would either of them follow me? I glanced toward the living room. Mother was trying to get Dad to come to bed.

My lies had worked!

It didn't take me long to get into my pajamas and fall asleep. The next thing I knew, Mother was trying to awaken me.

''Oh, no,'' I said, ''is it time for school already?''

Mom laughed. ''It's lunchtime! I let you sleep in. You looked so absolutely beat last night that I figured the sleep would do you more good than the classes.

But I think you ought to go this afternoon. I'll write a note and say you were sick.''

I didn't reply, but that didn't keep me from thinking that my mother was a liar, as well as a thief. *Is that where I learned it?* Well, I felt sorry for her. She had a miserable life, with that stinking drunk she was married to.

I hurriedly dressed and headed for the kitchen. Mom had a cheese sandwich and a glass of milk waiting. I wondered if she had changed the labels on the cheese package!

I didn't quite know what to do with all my money, so I decided to take it with me to school. I couldn't risk having either Mom or Dad find it. It would have been better if they had!

At school, the principal's office took Mother's note without question.

After school, I ran into Lillian. She was higher than a kite. When I asked her what she was using, she said she'd gotten some PCP, mixed some pot with it, and smoked it just before school let out.

I didn't want anything to do with PCP. I knew the stuff could get you high, all right, but it could also cause you to become a maniac. Besides, some of my friends at school were taking acid. You could see that their brains were frying—they were really freaked out.

"Sherri, let's stop by the pizza place," Lillian suggested. "I want to buy you a nice big pizza—a real big one, with everything on it. I owe you a favor, for including me in that deal last night."

Was it safe to be seen anywhere with Lillian? With her acting this way, would she loud mouth last night's deal? That's all I needed now!

I tried to make an excuse about having to get right home, but she just grabbed my arm and held on tightly. "Come on, Sherri, my friend. I don't have any real friends, except for you. You're my only friend."

I couldn't resist that. "Okay, let's go. But I just want one slice. I'm still thinking about that diet!"

"Okay. Okay, baby. Whatever you say. Why, if you wanted the whole pizza store, I'd buy it for you. You're my friend!"

We got our pizza and sat toward the back. With Lillian high, I didn't want to risk too many people seeing us. I had just taken the first bite, when I noticed a police car stop in front. I jumped up for a better look. Two cops—headed for the pizza-place door!

I yanked Lillian to her feet and dragged her to the women's rest room. I slammed the door and locked it.

"This isn't much of a place to eat pizza," Lillian protested.

"Shut up, Lillian. Two cops were headed our way!"

I leaned against the door, hoping against hope they hadn't spotted us. Minutes dragged on, but every minute that passed made it less likely they were after us. Maybe they were already gone. I decided to sneak a peek.

My hand was one inch away from the handle when someone pounded on the door. It almost scared me to death! "Open up, girls. This is the police. We want to talk to you."

"Lillian," I whispered, "if you have any drugs on you, flush them down the toilet. Quick!"

She reached into her blouse and pulled out three joints. I flushed them down.

Then I thought of that money in my pocket. How

was I going to explain that kind of money, if they frisked me and found it? One thing was sure: I wasn't about to flush money down the drain!

The police knocked again.

"Sir, this is the women's rest room," Lillian blurted out. "The men's is next door."

"This is the police," the voice came loud and clear. "We want to talk to you—now!"

Only one door led out of that rest room. No windows. We were trapped.

Lillian was enough aware of reality to begin slapping cold water on her face. I guess she wanted to look as straight as she possibly could. I didn't think it would help much.

"Sherri, what on earth am I going to do?" she wailed. "I'm high. I can't afford a bust. What am I going to do?"

I was too worried about my own skin to answer. I knew if they found me with that money, it was curtains. I would have to pay for my crime—and pay dearly.

Then I got this bright idea. Why not make Lillian the patsy? Maybe that way I could save my own skin.

I gently edged her toward the door. She was too high to have any idea what I was doing. As I unlocked the door and pulled it partially open, I carefully hid.

I heard one of the cops say, "Okay, lady, you'll have to come with me." With that, he grabbed her arm and led her away. I could hear the three sets of footsteps moving back into the main part of the pizza place. My scheme had worked. I silently congratulated myself on my cleverness. I could outwit cops any day.

I quietly shut the door and locked it. I could afford to wait.

I could still hear them talking out there in the main room—but not clearly enough to tell what they were saying. I couldn't pick up Lillian's voice at all. At least she knew enough to keep her mouth shut.

Finally, silence. Was it safe to go out? I'd better wait a little longer.

Then I heard footsteps again—approaching the rest room. Were they coming back?

Someone tried the handle—nothing. Maybe it was just someone wanting to use the rest room. Should I yell that the room was occupied? No, they could tell that.

I kept my eyes on the door handle. I couldn't believe it—the knob was moving! Before I could grab it, to lock it again, the door pushed open. There stood the owner of the pizza place, and behind him was a cop.

"Thanks, Louie," the cop said. "I thought there was another one in here."

The cop grabbed my arm and pulled me out of the rest room. I tried to protest, but he already had my arm twisted behind me and was pushing me down the hall, out of the pizza place, onto the sidewalk, and up to his car.

I glanced inside the police car and spotted two boys sitting in the backseat. I couldn't believe it—Maurice and Larry! Had they found out about that first night's robbery?

Larry pointed at me. "That's her, officer. That's Sherri Lenier. And the other one, the one that's high, that's Lillian Tolfon. They're the two you're looking for!"

With one motion, the cop grabbed his handcuffs, spun me around, and clamped them on me. Poor Lillian; she was already cuffed.

"Thanks, boys. We'll be in touch. Sure is good to find some kids who believe in law and order." With that, the officer opened the door and those two dirty rats got out.

As he passed me, Larry stuck his face almost against mine. "Sherri," he said, "everybody at school knows how you and Lillian knocked off Judge Walker's place last night. Aren't you ever going to learn that crime doesn't pay?"

I was so stunned, I didn't answer—although I felt like strangling him. How on earth did Maurice and Larry find out?

By this time, Lillian was straight enough to know a little of what was going on. "We didn't do it! We didn't do it, officer!" she protested. "Those sleazy characters are lying!"

"Quiet!" the officer ordered, and with that, he pushed her up against the squad car and began to frisk her. I knew I would be next, so I screamed, "Okay, officer, cut that out. I know my rights. You're not allowed to frisk a woman unless you're in the presence of a policewoman. Get your hands off her!"

He looked at me angrily, but he dropped his hands.

I wasn't nearly as certain about my rights as I sounded. I had seen a TV documentary about it, and I hoped I'd said it right. At least, the officer stopped, and I knew I was safe—for right now, anyway. If they found over $600 on me, I knew I was in for trouble.

The officers then pushed Lillian and me into the car and took off. I looked forlornly out the window, as

Maurice and Larry sauntered off, grinning like cats that had just finished the whole bowl of goldfish. So help me, if I ever got out of this one, I was going to steal another gun and use it to blast both of them.

Lillian leaned over and whispered, "How did they find out?"

I put my finger to my lips.

Ignoring my signal, she whispered, "I bet I know what happened. The cops always go looking for the most logical people. They're probably on to Maurice and Larry, and those two were mad at us because Willie cut them out of the deal. Maybe Willie even told them he didn't want to see them anymore!"

That was probably it. I was learning that you could never trust another thief. I wondered if Lillian would break under pressure.

Down at the police station, they took us to two separate rooms for more questions. I sure didn't admit anything, and I don't think Lillian did, either.

Or did she? Because the next thing they did was take me to family court. It was just the judge—no jury. But what a judge!

"Young lady," the judge said, "the officers tell me that you're not going to admit to stealing. Well, I just wanted you to know that my name is Judge Walker. Those were my guns you stole last night."

What I feared most had happened. I wished the floor would swallow me up!

"It is in my power to send you away to the state training school for as long as I think necessary," he went on. "Or I can give you another chance. I see that you have no previous arrests. But before I decide, will you admit to stealing those guns?"

I studied the floor. My heart beat like crazy. Was this a trick? Was this really Judge Walker? Had Lillian squealed?

If I said I stole the guns, then he'd know I was guilty. Maybe then he'd really throw the book at me. But if I stayed silent, would that make him madder? Could they really prove anything?

I decided to keep quiet.

"Young lady, I'm waiting for an answer. I've got all evening, so you just stand there and think about it. It's going to be bad for you, if you don't confess."

Maybe I should admit it and get it over with. Maybe he would show mercy.

Then I thought about Willie. If I said I stole the guns, then the judge would want to know where they were. That meant putting the finger on Willie. If I did that, I'd be putting myself in the same position as that girl who came up missing. I'd be Willie's next victim. No way! I had to keep quiet!

"Okay, Sherri Lenier, I'm going to make a deal with you. I have every reason to believe you took those guns. But since you're not going to talk, I'm going to have the officers place you in a cell. You can do some thinking there."

He turned to one of the policemen. "Officer Clarkson, if she changes her mind and wants to talk, let me know. I think she needs to do a little thinking about her future."

They led me down a little hall to a room. I wondered why they hadn't frisked me yet. Maybe they wouldn't.

But in that room, two policewomen waited for me.

"Okay, lady, strip!" one of them ordered—with the gentleness of an elephant. "Before we put you into a cell, you have to have a physical."

I'd heard about the indignities a woman prisoner faces. The whole idea of stripping, with them watching—and all the rest that went with it—almost made me ill. It would be better to confess, than to go through this.

"Okay, okay. Just hold it a minute!" I yelled. "Take me back to Judge Walker. I'll tell him the whole story."

"Well, well, a change of heart already?" one of them asked sarcastically. "But sorry, we can't do that now. The judge is busy. Maybe in three or four hours he can see you."

I had to think of another angle. I couldn't risk having them find that money!

"Okay, okay," I said. "But why not just let me wait in his courtroom? I'll be quiet. You can even put hand-cuffs on me. I promise you, no trouble. That way, the judge can talk to me whenever he has the time."

"Nice try, kid," one of them laughed. "But we just don't do things that way here. Now strip!"

No way was I going to strip! I just stood there.

Then they both pushed me up against the wall and started unbuttoning and unzipping. One of them felt the bulge in my jeans pocket. She reached in and pulled out the wad of money. "My goodness, girl, wherever did you get this kind of money?"

I wasn't about to tell her!

Since they had already found the money, I decided I'd better cooperate. I pulled off everything and stood there naked, as they searched through every piece of my clothing.

When they didn't find anything else, they put the

money in an envelope, sealed it, and wrote my name on it. One of them took it and walked out. I never saw the money again.

They let me get dressed, and when she returned, they both led me down a hallway and through a locked door. I saw the cells. They looked so creepy and awful.

One of them unlocked a door to a cell. It made an eerie sound as it opened. Then she gave me a little shove and slammed the door behind me. The noise ricocheted around—it sounded horrible. I was terrified.

All alone in that cell, I walked over to the bench and started to bawl. I wasn't faking it, this time. These were real tears. I was just sixteen—and already in jail. What would my folks say? What would the kids at school say? Why was I so stupid, to think that I was different—that I wouldn't get caught?

It seemed like a lifetime as I waited those three hours. Then the two women officers reappeared. "The judge is ready for you now," one of them said icily.

As I stood in family court again, Judge Walker peered down at me. "Young lady, are you ready to tell me what happened?"

"Can I make a deal with you, Judge?"

He smiled slightly. "All I want to know now is whether or not you stole my guns. Did you?"

I knew nothing about procedure—or even that the judge whose guns were stolen shouldn't have been handling my case. But I was ready to admit stealing the guns, if he wouldn't press me on what I did with them. I just knew that if I squealed on Willie, he'd kill me!

"I'm waiting," the judge said. "I'm interested to

know what kind of a deal you propose to this court."

"Just supposing . . ." I started, "just supposing I admitted to taking your guns. Would you demand to know where they are now?"

"Then you are admitting you took the guns?"

"Hey, wait a minute, sir. I didn't say anything like that. I just asked you a simple question. Do I have to tell you what I did with those guns—that is, supposing I did take them?"

He sat there for a moment, studying me. "Young lady, I think we need to get something straight. I know this is the first time you've been in a courtroom, and I think you've learned a valuable lesson. You've caught a glimpse of what it's like to be in a jail cell. I've had the horrible burden of sentencing many young women to do time behind bars. Let me tell you, it's no picnic. Being in jail is one of the worst things a person can experience. You have no rights. You do what the prison people tell you. Jails are crowded, and you're thrown in with the worst of humanity. Even when you get out, that unbearable experience of being known as an ex-convict follows you forever. You may think you've paid your debt to society, but that debt is on the installment plan—and you'll be paying it the rest of your life! There's no way you can erase your past!"

I stared at the floor, ashamed to look him in the eye.

"All I want you to do, young lady, is to admit you took those guns. I'm not all that concerned over the guns. They're covered by insurance. I can get more guns. But what I'm really concerned about is you and your future. Are you ready to answer?"

As I looked up at him, tears formed. I felt like a little girl, being reprimanded by a kindly father. I felt so small, so ashamed of what I had done.

"Yes, Your Honor, I took those guns."

"Now that's better. And I know what you did with them. You sold them to a fence. Now I'm not going to say who that fence is, but we've got our eyes on him. One of these days we're going to get him good, for steering young people into a life of crime. And I'm warning you, young lady, you'd better stay away from these fences. They're brutal, vicious men. They'll stop at nothing!"

He wasn't telling me anything I hadn't already heard!

"Do you understand me?" he demanded.

"Yes, sir, Your Honor. And I promise I will never again get involved with stealing anything. Never. I will try to be a good student and a good daughter to my parents. I promise you I will never, never again end up in court. I promise!"

Judge Walker took off his glasses and rubbed his eyes. "Well, I've heard it before," he said. "But maybe this time it will work."

"Yes. Yes, Your Honor; this time it will work. I promise!"

"Okay, then, you're free to go," the judge said. "One of the officers will take you home."

After the formality of filling out papers, one of the officers took me to a police car. "Do my folks know about this?" I asked him.

"Yes, ma'am. That's normal procedure, as soon as we pick up a juvenile."

"You mean you told them? You told them I stole guns?"

"Yes, ma'am. That will all be part of your court

record. And let me tell you something: You were lucky—really lucky. Judge Walker isn't always that lenient, even with first timers. You'd better thank God that you're going home free, rather than being locked up for a few years!''

The luck I had no trouble with. But I didn't know how to thank God. Did He really care if I stole? Did it make any difference to Him?

About two blocks from my home, the officer pulled to the curb. "I live farther down," I told him.

"I know that," he responded, "but I want to give you a break. You probably have nosy neighbors, just like everywhere else. If they see you get out of a police car, they'll be starting all kinds of stories, so I'm going to let you get out here and walk home. But if I find out you didn't go straight home, you're going to be in big trouble.''

"You don't have to worry about me now," I said, as I got out of the car. "And, hey, I appreciate this. I really do. You're an okay guy!''

"Save the sweet talk," he told me. "There's something else you ought to know. I was in the police car that chased a Jaguar out by the judge's house last night. I have every reason to believe you were in that car. We know all about Willie and his operation, and one day we're going to bust him. You'd better stay away from him, if you mean to keep out of trouble!''

I didn't dare respond to that. I couldn't afford to have them put Willie away, based on my testimony. So I merely told him I'd be careful and walked toward my house.

The officer stayed there and watched me. Was he

wondering the same kinds of things I was wondering?
True, I had promised the judge I would go straight. Yet
somehow I had this haunting feeling that my career in
crime wasn't over yet.

Was I trapped?

7

The police must have called my mother to say I was on my way home, because she was on the front porch, waiting for me. She didn't say a word, however, until we were inside. Then she began to curse me and scream and carry on like a maniac.

"Sherri! Sherri! How could you do this to me? As if I didn't have enough problems, with your father and his drinking! And now this! Don't you know you're an absolute disgrace? You're a no-good, dirty, filthy thief!"

"Aw, lay off it, will you?" I yelled back. "You don't know how close I came to being sent away. I got a break from Judge Walker. You ought to be glad you don't have to visit me in some jail cell!"

"Glad? I think it would have been better if he did send you away! That would have been one less worry for me to face. I don't think I can stand this pressure of you and your father much longer!"

"Look who's calling who a thief!" I said, with all the sarcasm I could muster, and headed for my room. I'd been through enough for one day and felt completely drained, emotionally. I sure didn't feel like fighting with my mother!

In my room, I flipped on some music on the radio and stretched out on my bed. I was so tired . . . .

The next thing I remember hearing was my door slam open. There stood my father. I expected him to stagger over to my bed, completely drunk, but he just stood there.

Then he flipped on the light and yelled, "Young

lady, I hope you've learned your lesson! There's nothing I hate worse than a dirty thief. You ought to be hanged!''

I was wide awake now! I pushed myself to a sitting position and yelled back, ''Listen, old man, who do you think you are, to stand there and yell at me? You're nothing but a stinking drunk yourself! After all the grief you've caused this family, what right do you have to criticize me?''

He started toward me. I wasn't going to take this lying down, so I jumped toward him. He was swinging as he came, but I ducked. Then I doubled up my fist and hit him as hard as I could, in his stomach. He bent back in pain, and I grabbed him around the throat. That's when he jerked his knee up and hit me between the legs.

The pain was so excruciating I began to scream. Mom came bursting into the room. She saw me bent over, holding myself, and immediately sized up what was going on. She ran over, slapped my father across the face, and yelled, ''Don't you ever strike Sherri again! Don't you ever kick her like that again! Don't you know that will make her sterile?''

Apparently my father decided he was not about to take on both of us, and he left the room like a whipped puppy. I walked over and curled up on my bed—I couldn't straighten out because of the pain—and yelled, ''I'll kill that animal! So help me, if he tries something like that again, I'll grab a butcher knife and cut his heart out!''

''Sherri, stop that! That's absolute nonsense. Don't you know your father's a very sick man? He's an alcoholic. He can't stay away from drink.''

"I'm telling you, Mom, if he tries that one more time, he's never going to have to worry about alcohol!"

I felt Mom's hand sting my face. "I told you to stop talking like that, young lady!"

She had never done that to me before. Oh, I'd gotten my share of whippings, but she had never struck me across the face. I guess the shock of it brought a little sense back into my befuddled brain. I stared at her. The more I wanted to hate her, the more I pitied her. She had such a miserable life, and she deserved so much more. I don't know why she put up with my father, and I wasn't exactly making life any easier for her right now.

"I'm sorry," I told her, suddenly remembering my promise to Judge Walker, to be a good daughter!

"That's better. I've been keeping your supper warm for you. I'll bring it in here."

When she brought the plate of food, she sat down beside me and started to sob. I put the plate down and put my arm around her. "Mom, I really am sorry for what I said about Dad," I told her again. "I'm just so frustrated and uptight about what happened today. I'm so embarrassed. I feel sorry for you, Mom. I really do. I didn't think about what this would do to you."

She wiped her eyes and said, "It's okay, honey. Maybe the days ahead will be better. I don't think they can be much worse."

"Well, Mom, I can tell you one thing. They're going to get better for me. I've learned the greatest lesson of my life. So help me, I'm not going to steal anymore. You can count on that!"

She smiled weakly. "Well, honey, if you've learned your lesson, I'm halfway there. Oh, if your father would only stop his drinking! Then life would be so glorious."

"You really love him, don't you, Mom?"

"Yes, honey, I really do—in spite of his drinking. But it would be so much better if . . . ." Her voice trailed off in sobs once again.

I really don't know why I said it, but I told her, "Someday, Mom, everything's going to work out!"

It sounded brave—a lot more brave than I felt, or even dared to hope for. But I was determined to change.

Next day at school, I looked for Lillian. She was nowhere. The word was out that she had been sent to reform school. Seems she had been picked up several times before for stealing. Poor kid. I felt so sorry for her.

No reform school for me. I had learned my lesson. I kept away from the kids who would be a bad influence on me. I studied hard. Would you believe I even got a *B* in algebra? I think part of that was because the teacher saw I really was trying—even if I didn't completely understand all we were doing!

Following my junior year, I got some baby-sitting jobs and some housework. It was a lot harder, getting a few dollars that way, but it was honest work. I wasn't about to steal again and face the threat of jail.

Dad was able to keep his job. In fact, he even got a promotion. Oh, he still had his drinking problem, but I think the events at our house reminded him to keep things in control. Mom and Dad even discussed his joining Alcoholics Anonymous. Nothing came of it, but at least things were a little more peaceful around home.

I had fun during my senior year. I studied hard. I knew college was out of the question for me. I wasn't smart enough for a scholarship, and my folks sure couldn't afford to send me, so I planned on working as soon as I graduated—and I wanted to be ready for that. I didn't know what I was going to do, but I did know it would have to be something honest. No more stealing, for me!

My folks were so proud of me when I graduated. They came to the ceremonies, and would you believe my dad was sober?

Right after graduation, I got a job as a secretary at a growing company that manufactured electrical components. I started at the bottom of the ladder, but they said I could work my way up in the company. They would train me on the job!

A few months later, they hired another secretary— Teresa Skinner. I liked her right off the bat. She had such an outgoing personality and was a lot of fun to be around. And she was good-looking, too! You could always count on a lot of guys being around wherever Teresa was. I liked that, too, because some of them paid attention to me!

A couple of months later, Teresa asked me if I'd like to move in with her. She was renting an apartment, and her roommate had married. The apartment had two bedrooms, but the rent was too much for her to pay alone, on the salary she was making.

Here was my chance to finally get away from home. I talked it over with my folks. I couldn't believe they were actually in favor of it. Mom said she thought it would be good for me to be on my own for a while.

They wouldn't have been so open to the idea, if they had really known Teresa. She was a bit on the wild side, but for me, that was exciting. Wow, you should have seen the parties we had! That got me back on pot now and then, but I figured I was an adult now; I could keep it under control.

Every so often, Teresa would go over her head and get high on other drugs. I didn't condemn her—that was her decision; but it made me all the more certain I wasn't going to go beyond pot: too many hassles.

The two of us found we had a lot of time on our hands, especially in the evenings, so we began hanging around bars. I told myself I'd never have more than two beers, but frequently drank three or four—and once in a while, I'd end up drunk. That worried me. Was I going to become a drunkard, like my father? Was it some weakness that ran in the family?

One evening we met this guy at a bar. He bought us a few beers. I knew I had had too much, so when he invited us to go for a ride, I was glad to get out of there. The three of us were a little tipsy.

He didn't drive very far—just to a delicatessen, to buy a six-pack. We'd drive and drink, he said.

He left the keys in his car when he went in. Teresa turned to me and asked, "What say we book?"

"What do you mean, book? Delicatessens don't sell books!"

She laughed uproariously. "Naw, silly. I mean take off with this guy's car. He doesn't know us from Adam. I didn't tell him my name. Did you tell him yours?"

"I don't think so."

"Okay, then, let's take off with his car and have a little joyride without him. He's too drunk to know what's going on, anyway!"

So were we! I was too drunk to reason that we weren't just going for a joyride; we were stealing! But it simply sounded like a wild way to have fun.

Teresa didn't really wait for me to answer. She slid over behind the steering wheel, turned the ignition on, and took off.

As we drove down the road, we both broke out laughing, thinking about that drunk coming out and looking all over for his car!

Well, we had a joyride, all right. But it was getting late, and we had to go to work the next morning. What about the car? Should we just abandon it? Probably the guy would call the cops, and they . . . .

Cops! That's when it dawned on me what we had done! I didn't want to get involved in that kind of life again!

Teresa must have read my mind. "Listen, I have a great idea," she said. "We need a car to get to work, but we can't drive one that's hot. Why don't we just hide this one for a little while? After things cool off, we can drive it around. If someone picks us up, we can just say we borrowed it from a friend and were waiting for him to come back and get it. Okay?"

That made as much sense as anything could, under the circumstances. Certainly there would be no harm done. That way, it didn't seem like stealing; after all, we had just borrowed it. And it would be nice to have a car to drive.

About a block from our apartment, we drove into an empty alley and parked.

The next evening, after supper, Teresa said, "Hey, let's go for a spin in that guy's car we borrowed. Okay?"

"Great idea!"

I really didn't expect the car to be in the alley when we got there, but it was. And was it ever a beautiful automobile! Wow! The interior was crushed velvet— just gorgeous!

Teresa got behind the wheel, and we took off.

As we pulled up at a stoplight, I happened to notice this old jalopy pull up behind us. "Teresa, I think we're being followed," I said.

"Sherri, you've seen too many cops-and-robbers movies," she reassured me.

But I noticed she made a quick turn to the right— without signaling. The jalopy turned right, too.

At the end of that block, she turned left; so did he.

"Teresa, we're in deep trouble!" I yelled.

"Don't panic. Do you think it's the guy who owns this car? Try to check him out."

I tried, but I didn't really remember what the guy looked like, anyway. That was no help.

We had to stop at the traffic light ahead. The jalopy pulled in behind us, and the driver jumped out. I yelled to Teresa to take off, but she couldn't. The car in front of us was waiting for the light to turn green. We couldn't go anywhere!

The driver of the jalopy ran to my side, jerked open my door, grabbed me, and dragged me along the ground. Then I recognized him! It *was* that guy we had met in the bar!

I felt blood trickling from my knees, and they were starting to burn. That must have happened when he dragged me out of the car. But I was worried about what else he was going to do.

Teresa shut off the motor and nonchalantly walked over to where the guy was standing over me.

"You cheap little hustlers!" he yelled. "I should have called the cops on you last night. But those cops are so dumb they couldn't catch a mouse if he stole cheese. Now I'm going to . . . ."

Several people had gathered and were watching. I guess that big bruiser must have felt embarrassed about tackling two defenseless women, so all he did was talk. "I decided it would be better if I caught you myself and taught you a lesson. I ought to kick both of you clear across town! But I think you've learned your lesson. Now get out of here, before I run over both of you!"

Teresa calmly reached down, grabbed my hand, and lifted me up. "Guess we'll just have to walk again, Sherri," she said.

A fleeting thought ran through my mind: *How is this guy going to drive away two cars by himself?* But I knew I wasn't going to stay around and find out! He meant business, and I wasn't about to get busted for car stealing!

I took off, running as fast as I could, even though my bruised legs were about to kill me. I thought Teresa would be running, too, but when I turned to see what had happened to her, she was still walking, calmly and nonchalantly, as though nothing had happened. I waited for her to catch up.

"For crying out loud, Teresa, aren't you scared? Don't you know we almost got busted for car stealing?"

"Aw, calm down, Sherri. As soon as that dude said he wasn't going to call the cops, I knew something was up. He's probably been busted himself. Maybe the car's hot. That means the only thing he could do was look for the car himself. Use your brains, kid!"

Back in our apartment, Teresa lit up a joint and handed it to me. I took a long drag, wanting to get high, so I could forget the whole episode.

We had some beers, and then we got to giggling, as we retold the story of taking that guy's car. Suddenly it seemed very funny. We'd had a lark—and didn't get into trouble with the law, either!

But the next day something happened that really sobered us!

At work, our supervisor came around and said she was very sorry, but business was down, and she had to lay us both off. She blamed it on the recession and said she'd call us when business picked up.

Talk about being shattered! Neither of us had worked long enough to collect unemployment insurance. We had lived from one paycheck to another. Neither of us had set up a savings or checking account. All we had was our severance pay.

I tried to keep optimistic—like Mother did when Dad was laid off. But when we looked for other jobs, we found that the recession had hit most businesses. We weren't the only secretaries looking for work, and nobody seemed to be hiring.

We started buying cheaper food—eating mostly sandwiches, cereal, milk—stuff like that. But our severance pay was fast dwindling, and the rent would be due in a week.

Something had to give. Then I thought about Willie

and wondered if he was still in business. One good night of stealing guns would tide us over until we could get work. I sure wasn't going to apply for welfare, and I was too proud to go home.

I pushed the thought of stealing out of my mind. There had to be another way!

That night Teresa and I were out walking and passed the deli where we had taken that guy's car a few nights ago. We both started to laugh when we thought about that episode again. Then Teresa noticed a car parked in front, with its engine running and no one inside.

"You thinking what I'm thinking?" she asked.

She didn't have to wait for an answer. We both hit that car on the fly. She slipped behind the steering wheel, jammed the car in gear, and we roared out of there.

We had a new Pontiac Grand Prix! It was burgundy, with a white-leather interior. We'd gotten a cream puff, this time!

"Teresa, what are we going to do with this?"

"I don't know, Sherri, but I'm not going to give it up. Maybe we can sell it. We could use the bucks!"

She sounded so matter-of-fact about the whole deal. Had she done this kind of thing before? It was her idea that we take that guy's car. Come to think of it, she'd never told me much about her past. I knew she was a little older than I. Maybe I'd better see what I could find out.

"Teresa," I said, "you seem to be pretty knowl-edgeable about this car-stealing business. Ever do it before?"

"That's a laugh!" she responded. "I did time for auto theft at the reform school. But don't let that worry you. I'm not about to go back to that kind of life. I just thought maybe we could use this to get some money, to help us out until we get our jobs back.''

Oh, wow! Here I was, living with an ex-convict, and I didn't even know it!

"Sherri, I just got an idea," she went on. "The cops will be looking for this one. We can't say we just borrowed it, so let's drive over and leave it in the rich section of town. The cops don't look for stolen cars over there. I remember an almost deserted little road, back in the woods over there. We'll just park it there for a few days. Then after the cops get tired of looking, we'll think of something to do with it.''

Teresa drove over to where all the estates were. It brought back a lot of memories about breaking into Judge Walker's home, but I stifled those thoughts. After all, we were broke, and we just needed a little money to help tide us over. It wasn't as if we were professional thieves.

We drove around the area until Teresa finally spotted the little lane that went back into the woods. We drove down there and discovered it only made a loop and joined the main road again. There was a little clearing off to one side. We pulled in there and parked. She locked the car, and we walked away.

"So help me," she said, "those cops will never come into this area, looking for a stolen car!"

We had walked a few blocks when a car approached, going our way. Teresa stuck out her thumb. The car stopped.

The well-dressed driver asked, "Aren't you girls scared to be out here hitchhiking?"

"No," Teresa answered calmly. "This is a really nice neighborhood—really safe. We were visiting some friends, and the party got sort of wild, so my friend— Betty Hawkins—and I decided we'd better leave. Sure appreciate your picking us up, mister."

The man was so concerned about our safety that he drove us to the address Teresa gave him, which was about a block away from where we lived. She told him a different apartment building, just in case somebody found out and traced us to the neighborhood.

A few nights later, we walked a few blocks and stood across the street from Dunkin' Donuts. Every so often, somebody would drive up, leave the engine running, and dash inside.

"The next time someone does that," Teresa said, "we're going to get our second car."

It was only about ten minutes until it happened. Teresa and I ran across the street and took off with the car. We drove straight to the clearing across town and pulled up behind the Grand Prix. We got out, locked this one up, and started walking again.

Before long, a car stopped when Teresa put out her thumb. This time it was a lady. Teresa told her the same story—no problem. The way people believed that story, they must have been aware of a lot of wild parties in that neighborhood!

The days sort of melted into weeks. I don't really know how long it was. Our landlord told us he'd carry us a little while on the rent. We had always paid on time, before. Besides, he still had our deposit, so he wasn't all that worried.

Another night we picked out a different deli. This time we got a Cadillac. We drove across town to our two deserted cars and pulled the Cadillac in beside them.

"No walking away, this time," Teresa told me. "Let's take the Pontiac. The cops have so many stolen cars to worry about that I think we can get by with this one."

So that night we drove back and parked near our apartment.

The next night we took out the Pontiac to go touring around and pulled up across from Dunkin' Donuts and waited. Half an hour later, a guy pulled up and ran inside, leaving his car with the engine running. "Go get it!" Teresa told me. "I'll meet you at our special hiding place."

With that, I ran across the street, jumped in the car, and took off. Just as I hit the street, I looked in the rearview mirror. The windows were open, and I heard the guy yelling, "Stop! Stop, thief!"

I should have taken that as a warning, but I didn't. All I could think of was that I had to get out of there—fast! I knew Teresa had taken off in the other direction.

Oh, no! Up ahead, the light was red. That guy was probably running in my direction! He could overtake me, and I'd get busted! To my right was a huge parking lot for a shopping center. I turned in and went speeding across, narrowly missing several cars. I hit the side street and—oh, no! Another traffic light. But this time, it was green. Now if it would just hold . . . .

I jammed the accelerator to the floor and went speeding through the intersection, just as the light turned red. I glanced in my mirror, hoping there were no cops around and relieved that no one had started through the intersection when I came barreling through!

I was far enough away now that I could slow down. I couldn't take a chance on a speeding ticket!

When I got out to our "used-car lot," as we now jokingly called it, Teresa was waiting.

"Great!" she said, as she congratulated me. "We're getting to have quite a business here."

We both laughed. The whole thing was ridiculous. Here we were, two unemployed secretaries, stealing cars and storing them on a deserted road in the rich section of town. And the police didn't have a clue!

We got two more the next night. I couldn't believe we had six cars—five parked, plus the Grand Prix we were driving.

"Teresa," I said, "we have all these beautiful cars, but we're not making any money. What in the world are we going to do with these cars? We sure don't need six of them to drive around!"

She laughed. "It's simple. Tomorrow I'll show you."

I wondered what she had in mind, but knew better than to ask too many questions. Well, I wish I had asked—because it turned out to be an experience I never will forget. I thought we were going to get ourselves killed!

8

We slept late again, then Teresa said, "Come on! We're going to go for the ride of your lifetime!"

We drove out to our "used-car lot," left the Pontiac, and climbed into one of the older models. Then we headed out of town and onto a dirt road.

"Fasten your seat belt!" she ordered.

"Do what?"

"Fasten your seat belt and hang on!" With that, she floored it.

I wheeled around. Were the cops after us? No—no one was in sight.

Now I knew what she meant by the ride of my life. She obviously was going to see how fast this car would go. But why on a bumpy dirt road like this? I'd read about kids speeding down dirt roads and losing control of their cars—and ending up splattered all over the road. That wasn't my idea of a good time!

"Teresa, if you want to see how fast this will go," I yelled, "please let me out first. I'll wait for you to come back, or I'll be ready to call the ambulance."

"Come on," she laughed. "I'm no dragster."

Well, she *had* slowed down. I guess we must have been doing about forty-five. All of a sudden, she yelled, "Hang onto the seat!" With that, she headed for a mailbox on a post. She was going to hit it on my side. I screamed and covered my face.

I heard this loud crash. Through the corner of my

eye, I could see the mailbox and post go hurtling through the air.

We bounced along the shoulder, the car almost out of control. Teresa slammed on the brakes, and that made us slide alongside the road—sideways—to an abrupt halt. To this day, I don't know what kept that car from rolling.

I looked at her unbelievingly.

"Not bad! Not bad!" was all she said.

I began to swear. "You good-for-nothing idiot. What did you pull a stupid trick like that for? You get your kicks knocking off defenseless mailboxes? You are absolutely the most stupid person I've ever been with! You could have killed us both!"

She just laughed. "Man, did you see that mailbox fly? I've never had one go that high before!"

"Come on, Teresa, get off it. What's the game?"

"The name of the game is having fun!"

I knew this wasn't just fun. She must have something else in mind, for she straightened out the wheels, and we headed down the road again. That's when she began eyeing the telephone poles.

"No! No! Teresa! For crying out loud, did you take acid, or something?"

She turned toward me. "Come on, Sherri. Look at my eyes. I'm as straight as can be."

She began to pick up speed, all the while eyeing those telephone poles. Then she slammed on the brakes, and once again, we went skidding off the road, narrowly missing one of those poles.

Before I had a chance to recover from that near miss, she jammed the car in reverse and headed back toward the pole we had missed. "Squat down," she yelled, "or the impact will jerk your head off!"

She didn't have to tell me twice. I didn't know what this maniac was up to, but . . . .

Crash! My head shot backwards, hitting the back of the seat. Every bone in my body seemed to burst with pain.

Then I glanced over at Teresa. I couldn't believe her—she was sitting there, grinning. "That's much better," she said. I turned around and could see the trunk lid was pushed up and the back window cracked.

No more of this for me. I unhooked my seat belt and jumped out. "Absolutely no way am I going to get back in that car with you, you maniac!" I yelled.

"Okay, have it your way." She took off, leaving me stranded. It was going to be a long walk back to the apartment, but at least I was still alive!

Then I noticed her turn around and start back toward me. Was she going to run me over? No, she veered off toward that telephone pole again. She hit the brakes, and the car skidded in the dirt, hitting the pole with a loud *crack!*

Now the front bumper angled up into the air. Glass and metal fragments flew over the hood. *That stupid girl. She must be trying to kill herself.*

I couldn't see her moving, so I rushed to the car and tore open her door. She just sat there, laughing! "This is the best fun I've ever had. I always enjoy this part!"

"Okay, Teresa, you ready to tell me what's up?"

"Hop in, kid. We're about to make ourselves a few fast bucks with this heap."

I couldn't believe this "heap" would even run now. But it rattled and wheezed to a point where we turned off onto another dirt road and pulled up in a junkyard. I was beginning to get the picture.

Teresa stopped in front of an old shack, and a greasy-looking guy ambled out.

"Hey, Sam," she called, "what do you think of this beautiful junker?"

"Well, Teresa! Good to see you again! I must say, you're doing as good a job as ever with these old wrecks. But it's a dangerous business you're in."

Then he noticed me. "Who's your accomplice?"

"Uh, Sam, this is my roommate, Sherri Lenier. Sherri, this is an old friend of mine, Sam Kleinert."

"Don't tell me you were in this old wreck with Teresa?" Sam asked. "Looks like you got out without a scratch."

"Well, after the first big bang, I became a spectator," I told him.

"Smart girl," he replied. "I never did feel safe, riding with Teresa!"

Then he pulled out a wad of bills. "A hundred bucks is all I can give you for it," he said. "The junk business isn't very good right now."

"A hundred bucks?" Teresa echoed. "You gave me two hundred dollars a couple of years ago. This one should be worth at least three hundred dollars. The motor's still pretty good. It's got an eight-track, air conditioner, power steering. Look at those tires— practically new. And those wheel covers—they don't make them like that anymore. I even saved a door and the windshield for you. Come on, Sam! This one's worth a lot more than a hundred bucks!"

"Okay, I'll make it one-fifty. But that's all, Teresa. It's pretty hot right now, and I have to watch my contacts. I think you know what I mean?"

I knew exactly what he meant. This junk dealer was making some easy money on the side. He'd take a wrecked car like this, and in about an hour's time, he'd have the engine out and all the parts laid out beautifully. He'd get all the usable parts off it, and the damaged parts would go for scrap. After a guy like Sam got through, the cops could never find a trace of the stolen car.

Teresa settled for the $150. "Better than nothing," she said. There really wasn't much else she could do with that car now, anyway.

The landlord was waiting for us when we got home. Teresa handed him $140. That would keep our apartment a little longer. With the $10 left over, we bought a few groceries, but we were still broke.

"You planning to do the same thing tomorrow?" I asked Teresa after supper.

"Sure am," she replied. "After all, one hundred fifty dollars a day isn't too bad, for two little secretaries!"

"But, Teresa, don't you know you're likely to get hurt? That first time, we almost went out of control. You could've easily rolled that car and ended up underneath it. There have to be easier ways to move those cars."

"Such as?"

"Well, I may have a contact where we could get more than one hundred fifty dollars for them."

"You know another junk dealer?"

"No, but a couple of years ago I knew a really smart fence. He lives over in the part of town where I grew up. Maybe he could take those cars off our hands or knows someone who would. Why don't we try that first?"

"Great idea!" she responded. "Let's head over there now."

"Okay, but we're going to need some wheels," I said. "You know that drugstore just over a few blocks? I bet it would be a great place to shop for a car!"

"You have quite a sense of humor!" Teresa answered. "Come on! Let's go!"

In minutes, we were at the drugstore. We stood outside, leaning up against the window.

"We're not being very smart," Teresa said. "If someone comes by and sees us here, he'll have a good look at us. We don't want that!"

So we walked about thirty feet away, stepped between two parked cars, and waited.

Within five minutes, a guy pulled up and double-parked, leaving his engine running. No sooner was he in the drugstore than Teresa and I dashed to his car. "You drive," she said. "You know where we're going."

I threw the car in gear and slammed the accelerator to the floor. Tires squealed as we took off. I glanced in the rearview mirror. The guy hadn't even come out yet.

When we reached Willie's house and knocked on his door, he answered right away. "For crying out loud, Sherri!" he exclaimed as he hugged me. "Where have you been, baby? You been doing time?"

"No, Willie, nothing like that. Just being a good little girl."

"Who's your friend?"

"Willie, this is Teresa Skinner. She and I are room-mates. We were secretaries in the same office, and then we got laid off because of the recession. You know how that goes."

"Well, come on in, girls. Since you don't have jobs, maybe you could use a little bread—right?"

Teresa nodded. Then she asked, "Willie, don't you remember me?"

He studied her features. "You know, come to think of it, you do look familiar. Where have we met?"

"One time I brought you a TV set. A friend of mine told me about you. But when I came to your door, you acted like you never knew a thing about your game. I mean, you must have thought I was the cops, or something."

"Yeah, I remember that vaguely. A couple of years ago, I heard they were on my case, so I was being extra cautious. Yeah, I probably thought you were an undercover cop."

"Yeah, you rascal. You wouldn't buy that TV set."

"I apologize," he said. "But you know how it is; I have to be careful."

Then he looked at me. "Why did you come?"

"Well, Willie, we have five cars stashed, and we need to dump them quickly. Do you want them?"

He was on his feet. "Five cars?" he asked. "You two must have been really busy!"

"We had six. Teresa turned one into junk, and we only got one hundred fifty bucks for it. These are good cars. In fact, one of them is a new Grand Prix. I figured you could do better than one hundred fifty bucks."

"Well, I'll tell you, girls, I don't deal in cars. But I have a friend across town who does. Why don't you take me out to where you have your cars and let me check them out for him?"

When he found out our car was hot, he suggested we move it to the alley and drive out in his car. This time his car was a Mercedes. I wondered what had happened to his Jaguar. Maybe it was hot, too?

Willie followed our directions to where we had our cars hidden. There were all five of them, sitting there as pretty as can be.

"We call it our used-car lot," I said.

Willie thought that was pretty clever. He checked them over carefully, noting make and model. "I think I can get you three hundred dollars each for them," he said matter-of-factly.

"Three hundred each?" Teresa echoed. "Are you kidding? These cars are worth a whole lot more than that."

"I didn't say they weren't," he replied. "But remember, I have to sell them to someone else, and I have to make enough for the risk I'm taking. We have a few people to pay, you know."

"But, Willie—three hundred bucks? That's absolutely ridiculous!" Teresa acted as if she were almost in tears.

"Okay, okay," Willie responded. "For Sherri, here, I'll do the very best I can. I'll get you four hundred bucks each for the five sitting here, and another four hundred bucks for the one in the alley by my house. That's twenty-four hundred dollars. Not bad, right?"

I may not have done well in algebra, but I knew right away that was $1,200 for Teresa and $1,200 for me. That should tide us over until we find work!

Teresa and I looked at each other and nodded.

"Okay, it's a deal," I said.

"Now then, here's what I want you to do," Willie said. "We'll have to move them tonight. This guy I know owns an appliance store. Just back of his place is a vacant lot. Put them all there. If anybody asks what you're doing, just say Al Putnam said you could park there. Just act natural. Move all six of them there."

We had to go back to our apartment, to get the keys. On the way, Willie pointed out the lot where we were to leave the cars.

We got the keys and drove back to Willie's house. He paid us off in fifty-dollar bills.

"You sure trust us, don't you, Willie?" I asked. "I mean, we haven't even delivered the cars yet, and you pay us. Supposing we just took off with the money and the cars? What could you do?"

"You know better than that!" Willie answered. "There's no place on earth you can go that my contacts aren't able to get you. You hear what I'm saying?"

"Hey, Willie," I answered nervously, "I was only kidding. You know you can count on me to deliver those cars."

"Of course, you'll deliver those cars," he replied. "If there's one thing I can't stand, it's a dishonest thief!"

We drove the car we had stolen that night out to our used-car lot and spent most of the rest of the night shuttling the cars to their new location. When we got the last one there, it hit me. What were we supposed to do with the keys? I'd better call Willie.

"Just wait there," he said. "I'll be right over to get

them. Then I can take you back to your apartment."

I didn't relax that night until we finally were safe in our apartment. Each of us was $1,200 richer.

Teresa went into her bedroom and brought out a couple of joints. We lit up and got high—anything to calm those nerves.

It was past noon when we got up and around the next day. As I was fixing a piece of toast and a cup of coffee, Teresa said, "Hurry and get ready. I'm going to go down and open a checking account."

"Isn't that a little risky?"

"Naw. I'm not going to put that twelve hundred dollars in it—just fifty bucks. And with that, I'm going to make several hundred more."

"How are you going to do that?"

"Still full of questions, aren't you? Well, since you helped out so much on the cars, I think it's time for me to begin teaching you a few tools of our trade. There are thousands of ways to make money. This is one of the oldest tricks in the world."

"Tell me. I'll probably need to know."

Teresa laughed. "A good teacher doesn't tell. You have to learn by observation. Now come along with me, and keep your mouth shut. You aren't learning anything, when you're talking!"

That afternoon we headed for a nearby branch bank, and Teresa opened a checking account with fifty dollars. She opened it under a name I'd heard her use before—Betty Hawkins.

How in the world was she going to use that to get more money? All I could see was that she had given up fifty dollars. The checks weren't even in her own name. But since she had been so pointed about my asking questions, I decided I'd better let the matter ride. She'd tell me, when she got ready.

About 11:00 that night, she said, "Sherri, there are a couple of important matters we have to attend to tonight."

"Important matters? At this time of night? What are you talking about?"

"I told you to knock off the questions, Sherri. Come on."

Using our usual tactics, we soon had another car. Teresa drove to a town about twenty miles away and headed for an industrial area. She just kept driving around.

For the life of me, I couldn't figure what was up. But she acted nervous, so I figured I'd better keep my mouth shut.

Finally we pulled up in back of a small factory. "Come on," she said, motioning me out of the car.

I followed obediently. She was going to bust into this business; I could tell by the look in her eye.

She checked the windows for burglar-alarm systems. This one had wires all over the place. "Too risky," she announced. "We have to find a safer one."

We got back in the car and drove some more. "Watch for a new building," she told me. "One that looks like a new business just moved in."

"Like that?" I asked, and pointed to what appeared to be a new building just ahead.

When we got up to it, Teresa studied it for a moment. "Yep, I think this is what we want," she said.

We parked around back and checked for burglar-alarm systems. She motioned me to come to the door.

"Okay, I'm going to tell you something," she said. "These businesses that move into new buildings sometimes are so anxious to get moved in that they don't set up their burglar-alarm systems right away. Or maybe the burglar-alarm-system people are so busy they can't get around to installing it right away. So the guy moves in and sets up his business before he's burglarproof. And, baby, that makes this so simple!"

She pulled a small plastic card out of her purse, slid it in next to the lock, and wiggled it back and forth. The door opened: not a sound. No alarm!

"Some smart people sure are stupid!" I said.

I followed her to the front office, where she began to ransack drawers.

"Don't make a mess," she told me. "All we're looking for is their checkbook."

I began rummaging, too, and found it under some other books in a bottom drawer. "Hey, Teresa! What do you think these are?"

"Fantastic!" she said. "You got them!"

She thumbed through, until she got past the middle of the checkbook. Then she pulled out two pages of checks. There were three checks to a page.

"Hey," I said, "why don't we grab the whole book?"

"Listen, Sherri, if we stole the whole book, right away they would know their checks were missing, and they would stop payment on them. But if we take just a few out of the middle of the book, it's going to be days—or even weeks—before they know they're missing. We can have them cashed before then!"

So that was her angle.

"Next thing we have to do is find the check-stamping machine. You know—it stamps the amount of money on the check.''

I didn't know what I was looking for, but I kept rummaging through things. Then Teresa announced, ''I found it. Now I have to stamp my salary on each of these checks. Let's see; how much would I make in two weeks' time?''

She was looking at me for an answer. I didn't know what to say.

''Well, let's make it two twenty-one thirteen,'' she said. ''That sounds about right.''

''Yeah,'' I agreed.

She began pushing the buttons for $221.13. Then she put a check in, pulled the lever, and it stamped $221.13. She repeated that on the other five checks.

''Okay, let's put everything back, just the way we found it,'' she said. ''We don't want them to know their business has been broken into.'' She replaced the check-stamping machine and the checkbook and tidied up the drawers. Then we walked out, locking the door after us, got in the car, and drove off.

Down the road a couple of miles, Teresa pulled over. She took the checks and a pen out of her purse. ''Sherri, in the blank space where it says 'Pay to,' I want you to write 'Betty Hawkins.' That'll be me. Down in the lower left-hand corner, write 'salary.' And above the line where it says 'Treasurer,' sign 'Donna Wilsky.' You're going to be the treasurer of my company! See, Sherri, you're in the big time!''

I did as she instructed. Then she stuffed the checks back into her purse.

''Okay, we have one more matter to attend to tonight,'' she said. ''We have to get a driver's license made out to Betty Hawkins. And while we're at it, we might as well get one for you, too.''

''How are we going to get drivers' licenses at this hour of the night?''

''I have a good friend in the forgery business. He can make up as many as we want. Simple.''

When we drove up to a building in our town, Teresa told me, ''You stay here, Sherri. This guy will only deal with people he knows. If I brought you up there with me, he would act as if he didn't know what I was talking about.''

''That's okay with me. I understand.''

Teresa went into the apartment house and about thirty minutes later returned to the car. She got in and handed me a phony license. It looked just like the real thing. My name, I discovered, was Violet Schneider. That wasn't much of a name, but what could I say? It was too late now.

''You owe me a hundred bucks for that, Sherri.''

''A hundred bucks? Isn't that kind of high for a driver's license?''

''Not when you can use it for identification and make yourself a few hundred with it,'' Teresa responded. ''If you ask me, that's a good investment!''

We slept late again the next day. That afternoon, Teresa told me she wanted me to go to the supermarket with her. I thought that was strange; we had just put in quite a few groceries after getting that money from Willie. But I knew better than to ask too many questions. She must have something up her sleeve. But I still couldn't see how all these pieces were going to fit together.

9

When we walked into that huge supermarket, Teresa headed for the candy counter. She found the bubble gum and bought two packages.

Second childhood? I wondered.

Next she grabbed a shopping cart. As she did, she tossed me one of the packages of bubble gum. "Chew that, and chew it well!" she ordered. "Whatever you do, keep chewing until I give you further instructions."

Both of us started chewing furiously as we put a few staples into the cart.

The gum tasted good—it did remind me of some of the few pleasant experiences of my childhood. But my jaw was beginning to ache from chewing such a wad of it at one time. Of course, I couldn't resist blowing bubbles now and then.

"Stop that!" Teresa ordered. "You're making a spectacle of yourself. All I need now is for you to blow a bubble and have it burst all over your face and hair!"

I wanted to tell her that the whole thing seemed stupid, anyway.

With the few staples in the cart, Teresa headed for the place where they cash checks. Was she going to cash one of those stolen payroll checks? I guessed not, for we passed right on by the window and went down another aisle. She must have chickened out.

"Okay," she said to me, "I'm going to cash one of those payroll checks. But I need your help. When we went by there a minute ago, did you notice a little machine that takes your picture? You know what I mean?"

"No, I didn't notice any machine that takes pictures. Was it right out there in front?"

"Oh, Sherri, you little dummy. You have to keep your eyes open, in this business. Now go walk by that place again. Act as if you're looking for some more groceries. But look closely, and you'll see a little black box. It has a long stem on it, and right in the middle of the box is a tiny lens. Now go check it out. I'll meet you back here."

Teresa gave me a shove. I could tell she was nervous again. That always made me a little nervous.

I walked back down the aisle, toward the counter where the lady was cashing checks. Sure enough, there was that little black box. Yes, I could see right where the lens was. I acted as if I were checking some prices on boxes of cereal and then walked back to where Teresa was waiting.

"Okay, I saw it. Now what?"

"Now I'm going to go up there and ask her to cash this check. Since it is made out to Betty Hawkins, I will show her my phony driver's license. She'll take it, to write down the information. While she's doing that, I'm going to push my purse over the counter, so it falls at her feet. Now, when she bends down to pick it up, you take your bubble gum and push it on that lens."

So that was it. When they took Teresa's picture after they cashed her check, all they would get was a picture of a wad of bubble gum!

"Very clever! Very clever!" I said admiringly.

"Don't get your hopes too high," she cautioned.

"This one has been done before. So let's hope this lady isn't too alert. Because when that check comes back and they find out it was stolen, they'll start going through their files for the picture. So you have to do this right. You think you can handle it?"

I had that funny feeling in the pit of my stomach again—just like when we were about to steal those guns, a couple of years ago. My promise to Judge Walker came back to haunt me. "I'd never steal again," I had told him. Here I was, making a regular career out of crime—almost. I was in this thing too far now; there was no turning back. *Why, oh why, did I get myself into such messes? What was wrong with me?*

As we walked up to the counter, Teresa asked, "Ma'am, would you cash my payroll check, please?"

"Sure," the cashier answered pleasantly. "All we need is some identification. Do you have a driver's license?"

"Sure do." Teresa took out the check, endorsed it, and handed it and her driver's license to the woman. Just then, Teresa turned toward me. As she did, her elbow "accidentally" hit the corner of her purse, sending it sliding across the counter and bouncing at the woman's feet. I could hear the things tumbling to the floor.

"Oh, my goodness!" Teresa said. "I was going to tell my friend that I forgot to get bread. Here. Let me help you."

She leaned forward, and the woman bent down. That was my cue. I quickly slapped the bubble gum onto that little lens and pushed hard, to make sure it would stick.

In a few moments, the woman had picked up the stuff from Teresa's purse. Teresa thanked her profusely for her kindness and made several comments about how clumsy she was today. The woman didn't say much—just kept on writing down the information she needed.

Then she said, "Okay, Betty Hawkins, if you will just stare at this little box, I'll take your picture, and then I'll give you your money."

Teresa smiled at the lens. "I always take pretty pictures," she laughed.

The woman didn't even look at the lens. She probably went through the procedure so many times every day that it had become automatic.

She counted out $221.13. Then, as Teresa was gathering up her money, she "accidentally" flicked a twenty-dollar bill over the counter. The woman bent down to retrieve it.

As she did, Teresa jerked the bubble gum from the lens, while saying, "Oh, my goodness. I certainly have 'dropitis' today: first my purse, now the money."

"Oh, that's all right," the lady responded. "We all have days like that. In fact, my husband says I can't hang onto money, either!"

We all laughed. It was corny, but it helped relieve the tension.

The groceries cost us $19.67. That was a pretty good investment, to gain over $200, as Teresa observed.

We put the groceries in the trunk of our stolen car and headed for a nearby small town and another grocery store.

"You going to do it all over again?" I asked Teresa.

She didn't answer.

Inside, I started to look for a candy counter and the bubble gum. Teresa told me to cool it; she wasn't ready for that, yet.

She flopped two big steaks into our grocery cart and headed for the check-cashing counter. Down the aisle from it, she suddenly stopped and whispered to me, "I smell something wrong here. That cashier looks too smart. I don't think we'd better try bubble gum. But here's another one for you."

With that, she turned and headed for the personal items. She picked a jar of Vaseline petroleum jelly off the shelf, opened the jar, and put a little on her finger-tip. She then returned the jar to the shelf, and we headed back to the cashier.

There we went through the same ritual as at the other store. Yes, the woman would be willing to cash a payroll check, if Teresa could identify herself with a driver's license. I could see the value of that phony driver's license.

They had a picture-taking machine here, too—one exactly like the one in the other store.

I knew my bubble gum was on the floor of the first store, or maybe on somebody's shoe, by this time. And I knew Teresa had thrown hers away when we packed our groceries in the car. I smiled to myself, as I thought that probably was on somebody's shoe now, too!

But what was Teresa going to do to keep from getting her picture taken?

Just as Teresa reached into her purse for the phony driver's license, she said, "Hey, lady, what's that picture on the calendar back of you? It looks like the place where I used to live."

The lady turned. "Oh, that's somewhere up in Vermont."

When the woman had her back toward us, Teresa pushed her finger toward the lens and smeared Vaseline petroleum jelly all over it.

The lady turned back toward us and asked, "Are you from Vermont?"

"Yeah, I sure am. It's got to be one of the most beautiful places in the whole country, don't you think?"

"Well, I've never been there," the lady answered, "but my son's gone skiing up there a couple of times. He says it's fantastic."

Teresa endorsed the stolen payroll check and handed it to the woman. She stamped it and carefully copied down the information from the phony driver's license.

Then she told Teresa to look at the lens. She made that same stupid comment about always taking a good picture. I couldn't quite figure out what she had done, but that jelly must had some affect on the lens.

Once again we got our money, paid for the two steaks, and headed for the car.

As we drove back to our apartment, I said, "I guess that jelly has some effect on the lens, right? Otherwise you wouldn't have posed for that picture."

"Right, Sherri. It's another simple little trick. The jelly puts the picture out of focus. It usually beats bubble gum, because bubble gum stands out too much, and sometimes the cashier can see it sticking out. Yet bubble gum is a little safer, because it completely blocks out the picture. The jelly just makes it sort of hazy. If you don't rub it on just right, they may still

catch a part of you—maybe enough to identify you—
so you really need to be careful.''

"You have any more tricks about cashing checks
that I ought to know about, Teresa?''

"Yeah, let me throw one more at you. Some stores
take your thumbprint. If you go around one of those
check-cashing counters and there's no picture
machine, then it's probably a thumbprint thing. Just
watch carefully, to see what people are doing. If it's a
thumbprint, get a very small piece of cellophane tape
and put it on your thumb. A couple of little strips will
obliterate the print.''

So far Teresa seemed to have all the answers. But
would they be enough to keep us out of jail?

Somehow I knew it wasn't going to be very long
before we got caught. A person couldn't steal as much
and as often as we were, without a slipup.

Teresa cooked the steaks for supper—and were they
ever delicious. They kind of reminded me how good
that one was that I stole from the food store—the one
that started me stealing. Why had I ever started it? I
knew I might get by with some things, but sooner or
later . . . .

I was so deep in reverie that when the telephone
rang, it almost scared me out of my wits.

It was Willie. He asked to speak to Teresa. I wondered what he had in mind and why he didn't talk to
me. Did the cops find those cars?

I listened carefully to her end of the conversation.

"Sure, Willie. No problem this time, since you
know me and I know you, right? You're not going to
turn down a TV set. Right?''

Then she listened for a while.

"Okay, Willie, I'll get it for you. And while I'm at it, supposing I can get a truckload of furniture? Can you use it?"

Another pause.

"Oh, great, Willie! I can see that you and I are going to get along just swell. It'll make a little bit of money for me and a whole bunch of money for you, right?"

Something inside me said *Run, Sherri!* I should have listened. I knew we were getting into this thing too far. No longer could I rationalize and say that I was just doing it to tide me over until I got a job. And yet I couldn't get up enough courage to get out of there. Fleetingly, I remembered praying to God when Lillian and I had stolen those rifles and I thought she was going to use one to kill a man. I promised to stay away from stealing, if He'd get me out of that jam. Well, I did get out of that jam—through the kindness of Judge Walker—and I had stayed away from stealing for a while. But now I was in this thing deeper than ever.

Does it really make a difference? I wondered. *Are the laws there just to protect the rich? Does God care what I do? Had He really helped me in that first mess, or was it just a coincidence?*

About that time, Teresa hung up.

"Willie has a customer who wants a new TV," she explained. "I told him we'd get one for him."

"What do you mean, get one for him? How would we know which house has a new set? Besides, those consoles weigh a ton. We couldn't lug one of those through the woods. It wouldn't even fit in our car."

"Trouble with you, Sherri, is that you don't have enough imagination," Teresa responded. "Now just stay cool. I've got a plan. Tomorrow we'll pull off this deal as slick as anything. I've been working around to this one. I'll give you just one hint. Remember that checking account I opened in the name of Betty Hawkins? Well, watch and see what becomes of it."

The next day, Teresa went out and rented a small truck. I figured that one out: it was so we could carry the TV set we were going to steal.

But where did she plan to get the TV set?

Right after supper, Teresa grabbed her purse and checkbook and said, "Come on! We're going to go into Ridgewood and buy a TV set for Willie."

"What do you mean, buy a TV set? I don't owe Willie anything. I thought we were going to steal a set."

"Well," she replied, "yes and no. There are many ways to steal. Just come along with me, little girl. You're going to gain a wealth of knowledge!"

We drove the truck the fifteen miles or so to Ridgewood, cruising around town until we spotted a small appliance store that was still open for business. Teresa parked just as close to it as she could get with the truck. I admired her ability to handle that vehicle. I guess there wasn't anything she couldn't do!

When we got inside the store, Teresa immediately made her way to where some TV sets blared. Then she spotted the big console—a TV set and a stereo record player. Was it ever beautiful!

A salesman ambled up and said, "Hey, that's a beautiful set, isn't it? And I can really make you a deal on it!"

"How much?" Teresa asked.

"Well, we've been selling that unit for eight hundred ninety-five dollars. We've sold lots of them at that price. But that's the last one we've got, and it's been our floor model, so I can sell it to you for six hundred ninety-five dollars, with the same guarantee and all.''

"Six hundred ninety-five dollars? That seems like an awful lot for a floor model. Can't you cut it down a little more?''

"Cut it down? Why, lady, I just cut two hundred dollars off. At that price, I'm not making enough to pay my overhead. The only reason I gave you that price is because I need to move it, to make room for the new models.''

"Well,'' Teresa responded, "I really like it, but I think that's too much money.'' Then she turned to me. "Come on. Let's try another store. I think we can beat this deal.''

She and I started for the front door, with the salesman right behind us.

"Okay, now listen,'' he said as we walked. "I'll tell you what I'm going to do—just for you. You seem like a nice person. I'll sell you that set for six hundred fifty dollars. But that's my rock-bottom price. At that price, I won't make a penny on it, but I have to move it. Just think—six hundred fifty dollars for that beautiful nine-hundred-dollar console.''

"No,'' Teresa answered, "I don't want to pay that much. My girl friend and I just moved into an apartment about fifteen miles away. We used to live around here. I've been by your place many times and have seen the signs for your big discounts. Since we still had our rented truck from when we'd moved, I thought maybe we'd drive up here and could work a deal. But I'm not about to pay six hundred fifty dollars.''

By this time, we were out on the street and walking toward the truck. But the salesman hadn't given up yet.

"Come on, lady. Just six hundred fifty dollars and it's yours. That's a fantastic deal."

"Listen," Teresa answered, "I've got three hundred fifty dollars cash on me. We can't even come close."

"Well," he responded, "don't you carry your checkbook? You certainly have a check, don't you?"

"Yeah, I have my checkbook. In fact, right now that's where I have most of my money—you know, for moving expenses and all. But I didn't think you'd take a check from someone from out of town."

"Of course we take checks. Most of our deals are by check. Come back inside. You'd better buy that set, because there's no way I'm going to sell that to anyone else for six hundred fifty dollars. I don't know why I ever let you talk me into that kind of a deal, anyway."

By this time, he had Teresa by the arm and was almost pulling her back into the store. She turned and winked at me. I was priding myself at keeping my mouth shut through the whole deal!

We walked back into the store, and the salesman wrote up the ticket. Teresa wrote a check on the account she had opened under her alias, Betty Hawkins. Then she gave him her driver's license with the same name on it. The saleman stamped the receipt paid, then he and another man loaded the set into the truck for us.

And to think I had worried about how we were going to carry a big console around!

When we drove off, Teresa burst out laughing. "I

can just see the expression on that guy's face when that check bounces," she said.

I joined her laughter; that would be funny.

"Now, Sherri," she explained, "whenever you want to pull off something like that, always do it in the evening. Then they can't call the bank, to see if you have sufficient funds in your account. And another thing: act like you really don't want it and you're doing the guy a favor to buy it. These small dealers get itchy and take big chances, if they think they're going to lose a sale. They're so anxious to sell that they'll take anything—even a bad check!"

"Yeah," I responded. "I noticed that you didn't even have to bring up the matter of paying by check. He did that himself."

"Good girl!" she said admiringly. "You're learning to be observant. You have to be that, in this business."

As we drove along, Teresa said, "Well, we got Willie's TV set. Now we need to get the rest of this truck filled up with furniture. We'll do that tomorrow."

The next day we drove the truck into a lovely residential area. Teresa spotted a woman pulling out of her driveway.

"Okay. That woman is either driving to work or going shopping or to a doctor's appointment. Let's circle the block. If it's still all clear, then we'll load the truck."

We circled the block, and then Teresa backed the truck into the driveway, right up to the garage door. We rang the door bell, to double-check. No answer.

Teresa pulled out a thin plastic card, slipped it into the door latch, and wiggled it. The door opened.

"Okay, start loading," she said. We took lamps,

small pieces of furniture, and accessories and loaded them in the truck.

I was terrified, walking out to the truck in broad daylight with the stuff. "Teresa," I said, "this is stupid. Somebody's going to see what we're doing and call the police."

"Not to worry, little girl," she responded. "But this is one thing I never could understand, myself. People will drive by and see this truck, but they'll just think that someone is moving. Neighbors just don't ask questions these days. No one will call the cops!"

Teresa headed for the bedroom and began looking for money and jewelry. She found another stereo unit and took that out. I took out some clocks, sterling silver, and expensive silver pieces.

We still had only about half a truckload when Teresa said, "That's enough. The rest of this stuff is either too heavy or it isn't valuable enough to fool with. Let's get out of here."

With that, she shut and locked the back door of the truck. We climbed into the cab and drove off. Nobody had come by to see what we were doing. I just couldn't believe we could pull off a heist like that in broad daylight.

Have things gotten so bad that people don't really care, or is it they don't want to get involved? I wondered. I had heard and read about robberies like this before, but here I had actually participated in one. We had loaded that truck in broad daylight, in the front of the house, with people driving by—and no one even questioned what we were doing! I guess nobody called the police; at least, we didn't see them!

That night, we headed for Willie's place with our

loot. I was almost hoping to hear a siren. I knew I was getting deeper and deeper into crime and, somehow, I had to get out. But I really didn't know how. I sure didn't want to do time!

Of course, I tried to rationalize what we were doing—that we were stealing from the rich and from businesses. *After all,* I told myself, *they could afford it. They had insurance.* But I couldn't get away from my conscience or from the nagging feelings of guilt. Instinctively I knew what I was doing was wrong and that somehow I would get caught and would have to pay the consequences for my crimes.

Well, we got to Willie's place, with no sirens. He seemed quite impressed and gave us $1,000 for the truckload—$500 for each of us. We helped him unload the stuff into an old garage next to the alley. With the truck backed right up to the door, it would have been hard for anyone to know what we were doing.

On our way back home, Teresa told me she didn't want to split money with me on jobs like that. "I've been providing all the brains," she said, "and I don't like these fifty-fifty splits. Besides, there's a risk involved, and I know how to watch out for myself."

I protested that I couldn't handle jobs on my own, but she said she felt she had taught me well and that I could make it. She said we could make more money splitting up and going our separate ways.

She had a sudden inspiration and suggested we knock off another small business on the way home. She wanted me to get my name on some stolen payroll checks.

So we drove into another nearby town and began searching for new construction. Once again, I spotted

the place. We were inside in no time. We quickly found
the checks and the check-stamping machine. I took
two pages of checks; Teresa couldn't resist taking one
for herself. It all went so fast it was almost unreal.

The next day, when Teresa took the rented truck
back, I decided that since I was going to be on my
own, I'd better get started. I picked out a grocery
store, grabbed a cart, and selected a few items. We
really had all the groceries we needed, so I got a few
luxury items, forgetting the calories involved. Oh,
well, I could start my diet next week! We'd been eating
pretty leanly, recently.

Then I headed for the place where they cashed
checks. I cased it but didn't see any picture-taking
machine: no need for bubble gum or Vaseline petroleum jelly. They must use the thumbprint method.
Good thing Teresa told me about that.

I watched as several people cashed checks, but
nothing happened. All they had them do was show
some sort of identification. There was no need for the
cellophane tape on my thumb. This was going to be
easier than I thought.

I walked up, endorsed the check with the name Violet Schneider, showed the woman my phony driver's
license, and that was it. She counted out the $221.13.
Then I paid for the groceries and walked out of the
store. I kept turning around, expecting someone to
come running out after me—nothing.

Teresa was already back in the apartment when I
returned. I told her the great news. "No picture-taking
machine; no thumbprints," I said. "It was so easy.
You ought to go over there and cash one of your
checks!"

Her mouth flew open. "You dumb, stupid girl!" she yelled. "I thought I could trust you. Didn't you check around for a hidden camera? You have to keep your eyes and ears open, when things go too smoothly. They might have taken your picture. Didn't you see anything?"

"Teresa, I didn't see anything," I responded nervously, "not a thing. And that lady acted so nice. There was no problem whatsoever. I just think they're a good neighborhood store and they trust people, that's all."

"Oh, Sherri, you're so naive that you're hopeless," she told me. "Nobody trusts anybody anymore. I just bet that they got your picture. And if they did, that means big trouble!"

In a short time, I found out Teresa was right. My way of life was in for a quick change!

10

After that check-cashing incident and all the jobs we had pulled, Teresa thought it would be better if we laid low for a while. We had hidden our stolen car—the one we used for our own transportation—over on that lot where Willie had had us take the ones we sold him. Someone said the store was a front for the mob.

Well, we both went stir crazy, sitting there in the apartment, so we decided one night to go get the car and go for a ride—maybe even take a chance on bringing it back to the apartment.

I was driving, this time, and Teresa wanted to go back to the apartment, to get some pot she had stashed there. Just as I started to look for a place to park out front, she yelled, "Drive on by, and don't look suspicious!" With that, she dropped to the floorboard.

I glanced around, but couldn't see a thing. But at the end of the block, when I looked in the rearview mirror, sure enough, a car pulled out and started after us.

"There's a car right behind me, Teresa. Should I try to duck it?"

"Is it a plain-green car with two guys in it?" she asked.

"Green car? I can't see what color it is. It's dark outside, stupid."

"Listen, sweetie, don't ever call me stupid!" she snapped back. "If my guess is right, it's your stupidity that got us into this mess! Now listen. That green car parked out front of our apartment—it had two FBI agents in it. I can spot them a mile away. So is it a green car, with two men in it, that's following us?''

I looked in the rearview mirror again. The two lights from the car behind almost blinded me. I couldn't tell what color the car was or if *anybody* was in it!

I turned right as soon as I could and looked in the mirror, nervously holding my breath. The car went straight. The corner streetlight showed me its color: blue.

"We're okay," I said. "The car went straight, and it was blue."

Teresa jumped back into the seat and yelled, "Get out of here as fast as you can!"

I pushed the accelerator, and we headed for the main highway leading out of town, as fast as we could safely go. I certainly didn't want to chance a speeding ticket—not in a stolen car!

Teresa kept glancing back furtively. Whenever a car came up behind us, she grabbed the edge of the seat. She was as nervous as a cat.

"We're hot! We're hot!" she kept repeating. "Oh, I just knew this was going to happen. They're onto us!"

"Come on, Teresa! How can you be so sure?"

"There are fifty thousand things we could have done wrong. Maybe they nailed Willie and he squealed. Maybe they've gotten a lead on the stolen cars. But what I think happened is that check you cashed the other day. That might have told them the whole story. Sherri, there's absolutely no way I'm going back to that apartment. Absolutely no way!"

"Well, what *are* we going to do?" I couldn't keep the panic from rising in my voice.

"I can't answer that—especially for *you!*" she said with a note of finality.

"Come on, Teresa. You're my teacher. Think of something. What did you do the last time the cops were after you?"

"Don't talk that way, Sherri. The last time, they caught me. That's when I did two years. No way am I going to let that happen again!"

I gripped the steering wheel. The moment of truth had finally come!

"Make a wide circle to the center of Manhattan," Teresa suggested. "I don't think they'll be looking for us over there."

We made a long circle, went through Teaneck and the Lincoln Tunnel into Manhattan, coming out on Thirty-fourth Street. I drove along to Forty-second Street—among all the porno movies, drug addicts, and prostitutes. The whole place disgusted me, and ordinarily I would have stayed as far away from it as possible.

"Pull over to the curb here," Teresa ordered.

When I pulled over, she opened her door and jumped out. "Sherri, baby, it's been good knowing you!" With that, she slammed the door and took off running.

Where was she going? Was she going to come back? Did she expect me to come with her? It sure didn't sound like it.

I jumped out and yelled after her, "Hey, wait! You don't have to do that! Come back!"

Too late. I had lost her in the crowd!

Now what? Teresa really must have thought she saw those two cops. Or was she up to something that I didn't know about? Was this her way of walking out on me? She had said I needed to be on my own, that we needed to go our separate ways. But why would she come here?

I stood there, trying to fight back the tears—and the fears—and wondering what to do next. This greasy-looking guy walked up and tried to sell me some drugs. I was too upset to think about anything like that now. I needed all the wits I could muster.

I told him to shove off. He gave me a menacingly mean look and shuffled away, turning around and eyeing me.

I knew I'd better get out of there. I got in and drove aimlessly. Where was I to go? What was I to do? What was going to become of me? I felt so alone, so helpless. Nobody cared where I was or what happened to me! I certainly didn't want to stay in this creepy area of Manhattan. I knew I couldn't take a chance of heading back to our apartment. Those FBI agents probably had the apartment staked out, waiting. If Teresa had really seen them . . . .

Then it hit me. Why not go home? It had been months since I had visited. Maybe there I could get away from it all. At least I'd have time to think. Anyway, the cops weren't looking for Sherri Lenier—they were looking for Violet Schneider—a person who didn't exist, except on my phony driver's license! I'd be safe at home!

I dried my eyes and headed back to the Lincoln Tunnel and New Jersey. About forty-five minutes later, I abandoned the car, got on a bus, and finally got home.

The front door was locked, so I knocked. In a few

minutes, my mother stood there in her robe, shrieking, "Sherri! Sherri! What are you doing here?"

"What do you mean, what am I doing here? This is my house too, isn't it?"

She laughed. "Of course, honey! Of course! This will always be your home. But, I mean, it's late. It's strange that you would drop by at this hour of the night. Is something the matter?"

That mother's intuition—they can almost always sense when something's wrong.

"Naw, Mom, nothing is really wrong," I lied. "It's, well, it's just that I had a few problems with my roommate."

"Well, don't stand out here in the cold. Come on in, honey. You can tell your mother about your problems. In fact, I've been really worried about you the last few days. I just knew something was wrong. What happened?"

"Well, nothing really bad," I answered, slumping on the living-room sofa. "You see, Teresa kept having these wild parties, with everybody getting high and stuff like that. You taught me not to use drugs, and I didn't. But my roommate just wouldn't stop, and neither would her friends. Of course, it was her apartment, too, so there really wasn't much I could say or do about it. But tonight I decided to call it quits. Everybody was getting high. Then one of those junkies decided they were going to have a Roman orgy. He started taking off all his clothes, and everybody else did, too. Can you imagine that, Mom? I'm too embarrassed to tell you what went on next. I've tried to be a decent girl, so that's when I walked out."

"Oh, honey, that's exactly what I would have done.

But I think you ought to call the cops and stop that kind of nonsense."

"Naw, Mom, I couldn't do that. They weren't hurting anybody—only themselves. The cops probably wouldn't do anything about it. It was just something I didn't want to be a part of."

"I'm proud of you, honey," she told me. "Your bedroom is still like it was when you lived here. Tomorrow we can go back to your apartment and get your clothes. I think it's about time for you to move back home, anyway."

When she mentioned going back there tomorrow, I shuddered. Those cops—if they were there—would still have the place staked out. I had to deter that trip!

"It's not that easy, Mom. See, I also lost my job, and I'm behind on the rent. The landlord said that after tonight, he was going to take all my stuff and use it to help pay the back rent. Besides, I didn't have much stuff. I think we'd just better forget the whole thing."

"Okay, honey; whatever you think is best. But my goodness, I had no idea you were having problems like that!"

She insisted that we have a cup of coffee together. It felt good to relax in our kitchen again. I asked her about Dad, and she said things were somewhat better. They had been worse, but they were better now. That seemed to be the story of her life—a whole series of ups and downs with Dad—mostly downs.

It was almost noon before I awoke the next day. Mom had some fruit and juice waiting and then started cooking some ham and eggs. Such a fancy breakfast—almost like I was a special guest. She must have really missed me. At least I had provided a sympathetic ear for her in her problems.

After breakfast, I grabbed a copy of *Woman's Day* and sat on the sofa in the living room to read. When someone knocked on the front door, I answered it without thinking. There stood two men. They flashed their badges, identifying themselves as FBI agents. Then they said they wanted to come in and talk to me.

What could I say? Mom was sitting right there in the living room. They stood very close to me, ready to grab me. Maybe they didn't really have anything on me.

"Oh, officers, you've come to the wrong place," Mother called. "We're not gangsters here!"

"Yes, we understand that, ma'am. But we have just a few questions we want to ask this young lady. Do you mind if we sit down and talk to her a little bit?"

"You sit right down," Mother said warmly, as she came to the door. "In fact, I just made some fresh coffee. I'll bring you some."

"Oh, no thanks, ma'am. We can't stay that long. We just want to ask a couple of questions, and then we'll be leaving."

I breathed an inaudible sigh of relief. Just a couple of questions. I knew I could think of some good lies for answers!

I flopped onto the sofa, and one of the officers sat next to me. The other sat in a chair across the room— by the door. Apparently he had decided he would be ready, if I tried to make a break for it. Mom sat in another chair near him.

The officer next to me reached into his pocket and pulled out a check. He held it in front of me and asked, "Did you ever see this?"

I studied it. "Ever see that check? Of course not.
Why? I see it looks to be a payroll check made out to
Violet Schneider. I don't know any Violet Schneider,
and I've never heard of that company. Why do you
ask?"

"Ma'am, please take a closer look."

I glanced at Mom. She was on the edge of her chair.
"Mom," I said, "do you know any Violet Schneider?"

"Not that I know of," she replied. "I once knew a
Lucy Schneider, but that was years ago. Do you suppose they are related? Lucy had a daughter, I think.
She might have been named Violet. But I don't think
so. Anyway . . . ."

The agent ignored Mom's rambling and turned back
to me. "Are you telling me that you don't know anything about this check?"

"What's there to know about it, sir? Is this Violet
Schneider in trouble or something?"

He stood and faced me. "I'm sorry, ma'am, but
you'll have to come along with us."

He grabbed my arms, pulled me to my feet, and
snapped handcuffs on me.

Mother began to scream. "What are you doing? You
must be imposters! Are you trying to kidnap my
daughter? I'm going to call the police!"

"Now just calm down, ma'am," one of the officers
replied. "We are the police. We showed our identification. All we're going to do is to take your daughter
down to answer some questions for us."

"Sherri," Mom said as she stroked my hair, "have
you done something wrong?"

"Mom, I'd swear on your grave I haven't done anything wrong. These men are just trying to do their jobs. I don't know what I can tell them about Violet Schneider, but I'll try to answer their questions. Don't worry. I'm sure I'll be back in time for dinner."

I wish I had felt as brave as I sounded!

Mom looked so embarrassed as they led me, handcuffed, to their green car. She stood there looking up and down the street. I knew she was hoping the neighbors weren't watching. I was sure they were. They always did.

The two officers drove me to the county jail and took me into a little room. There they took off the handcuffs. Then they brought me some paper and a pen and told me to take some dictation—in longhand. Then I had to write a whole bunch of signatures for them.

I ended up with pages and pages of stuff I had written. One of the agents compared the signature on the payroll check with my handwriting. Finally he said, "Why don't you just admit that you forged that check? We really have the goods on you, Sherri."

"Aw, get off it, you guys. You don't have anything on me, and you know you don't. I haven't done a thing."

"Well, let me refresh your memory," the agent responded. "We know that you and Teresa Skinner, a girl with a previous record, were renting an apartment together. We've been onto you for several weeks now. We know you've been stealing cars. We know you've passed bad checks. We know about the furniture you've stolen. Little girl, you've done the whole route, haven't you? Well, we're ready to throw the book at you. But if you cooperate, you might get off a little easier."

"What are you talking about? Cooperate? I don't have the slightest idea what you're getting at. You don't have a thing on me!"

"Okay," he said, "let me give you a few more details. You know your friend Willie, the fence? Well, it just so happens that we had his place staked out the night somebody drove in with a rented truck and unloaded a bunch of furniture and stuff. We traced that truck to you and Teresa. And we also moved in on Willie. We got that guy with all that stuff in his garage. You should hear him singing! He's decided to cooperate with the district attorney, and he's naming a lot of names. He says you're one of them. Yes, ma'am. Willie is singing your name, loud and clear. I mean, we really have the goods on you, this time!"

He let that sink in.

"I guess you think you gave us the slip last night, huh? Well, right now we have two agents over at your apartment. As soon as your friend Teresa comes back, it's going to be all over for her, too!"

So Teresa had guessed right. But here I was, being nailed to the wall, while she walked around free as a bird in Manhattan!

I almost blurted out that they'd have to go to Manhattan, if they wanted to get Teresa—but I caught myself. I knew they had me, but I wasn't about to admit anything, this time. I was going to hold out just as long as I could. Maybe they just suspected all these things. Maybe they didn't have proof that would hold up in court.

"All right, Sherri, I'm going to read you your rights," one of the officers said. "You don't have to say a word. But I'll tell you one thing. If you cooperate with us, we may be able to work things out, so you can plead to a lesser charge.''

"Such as?"

''Well, that will be up to the judge and the district attorney. But I think we can promise that if you will tell us about all that was going on, you won't have so much time to do in the slammer.''

The words *much time* echoed around in my mind and scared me half to death. Did they really have the goods to put me away? They seemed to have the details down pretty well. But were they bluffing about Willie? Maybe they wanted to get me to testify against *him*—instead of his testifying against me! Oh, no! If that happened, Willie would be out after me forever. Even if he were in prison, he still had his contacts, and they would track me down wherever I went, he said. I couldn't chance that. They were going to have to prove their charges in court. I wasn't about to confess to anything.

When I wouldn't tell them anything, they booked me and shoved me into a cell. I used my one phone call to tell my mother not to wait supper for me. Of course, she was horrified that I'd been arrested and told me again she didn't want anything to do with a thief.

Later, when my case came up in court, I had a legal aide assigned to me. My parents wouldn't hire a lawyer for me. They didn't come to visit me; they acted as if I didn't exist anymore!

When the judge called my case, the first witness against me was a girl. I thought she looked familiar. Oh, no! It was the girl who had cashed that phony check for me.

"Do you recognize this check?" the D.A. asked her.

"Yes, sir, I do."

"And did you get a good look at the girl who cashed this check?"

"Yes, sir."

"Is she in this courtroom now?"

"Yes, sir."

"Would you point her out for the court?"

"Certainly." The girl stood up, turned, and pointed at me. "That's her. The defendant," she said.

I was so embarrassed that I started to squirm.

Then the D.A. put in evidence a secret photo of me that was taken at the time I had cashed the check. Teresa was right!

They charged me with forgery, cashing stolen checks, stealing cars, and all the rest. Even Willie was at my trial—not as a spectator, but as a witness against me. I couldn't believe all he said!

The jury's verdict? Guilty. I was given a sentence of from three to ten years in the state penitentiary.

That was indeed a house of horror! From the very first, the lesbians are out to get you. Occasionally there would be stabbings—girls fighting over other girls. It was sick!

Then there was the system. You're subjected, like an animal, to all the rules. I went along and didn't say much. But all the time, I was seething on the inside for all the indignities of the system. It just didn't seem right for a girl like me to be thrown in with this dirty, filthy pack of humanity.

The whole system reeked with private deals and playing favorites. At times, even the matrons were involved with some of the girls. It was absolutely disgusting. And I had to be careful constantly—that I didn't end up stabbed!

I spent two years there—two of the worst years of my life. During that time, I became more like Teresa, learning all I could about a life of crime. But it worried me. All the girls would boast about the way they stole and how many things they had stolen without getting caught. It was always that one twist of bad luck that had put them behind bars. I wondered about that.

Because I hadn't created any problems, I was brought before the parole board after two years. I was one of the lucky ones; they paroled me. I think that my being white and living in suburbia had a lot to do with it. I'd hate to think where I'd be, if I had been born in Harlem!

When the day finally came for me to get out, I knew I couldn't go home. Some of the girls had their families welcoming them when they were released. I had no one. I knew my parents were ashamed of me and had written me off. Never once in those two years had they visited me or even written to me. So I decided I would have to make it on my own. Never again would I trouble them. I'd get lost in the world and come up with a new identity.

The prison department made arrangements for me to go to a halfway house. The girls who didn't have much to look forward to ended up there. It wasn't the best, but at least it wasn't like prison. It was run by some good people who were genuinely concerned about the girls. They tried to get them jobs. The prison grapevine said it was the best place to go, if you couldn't go back to your family.

When I got there, it didn't seem at all bad. Of course, it wasn't like home, but I did have my own room, and the windows and doors didn't have bars on them!

They gave me some leads on places to apply for jobs, but I was turned down at every one of them. Talk about discouraging! I quickly learned that most places don't like to hire ex-cons. They don't trust them, and their customers don't trust them.

I remembered what Judge Walker had said when I was brought before him for stealing his guns. He said you kept paying your debt to society on the installment plan.

Was there no way I could overcome the stigma of having a prison record?

11

Before I ever went to the halfway house, I had determined I was going to go straight. No more doing time for me! But two things happened that weakened my resolve.

One was a shopping trip that most of the girls went on.

I didn't go. I didn't have any money to buy anything with, so why go? Eventually I would have to pay for my room and board at the house, but I still didn't have a job.

When the girls got back from their shopping trip that night, of course they had to show off all their bargains. I really needed a new pair of jeans, and suddenly I knew how I was going to get them.

I had noticed that Janet had the most packages of anyone. After she had gone to her room, I knocked on her door and asked if I could see her for a minute.

"Sure," she said, inviting me in. Then she started in about the fantastic bargains she had found at Mays and began digging everything out of the bags and showing me again. I especially noticed one bag, where she left a sales receipt.

"Those are all so beautiful," I said, "and you really did get some fantastic buys! I'm so glad for you."

Then I asked if she minded if I took one of the empty shopping bags. "I need it to put my underthings in when I go down to wash them," I explained. "Last night there were some boys visiting some girls, and I was kind of embarrassed.''

Janet laughed. "You need a laundry bag," she said. "If I had an extra one, I'd give it to you."

"Oh, I'll get one, eventually. But until then, that big bag over there will work just fine—if you don't mind."

"Mind? As far as I'm concerned, you can have them all, if you want them. I'm just going to throw them away, anyway."

"Sure you don't mind?"

"Of course I don't mind. Here. Take them."

With that, she practically shoved them into my arms. I thanked her and took them back to my room. As soon as I got them there, I pulled out the old receipt and tucked it into a pocket of my jeans.

Later that night, when I was sure everyone was asleep, I walked downstairs, to a small, unlocked office. There were no valuables in it, but there was something there that was the key to my getting a new pair of jeans: a stapler! It was a small one. I stuffed it down the front of my jeans and covered it with my blouse. Then I went back upstairs to bed.

The next morning, I headed for Mays, with the stapler tucked inside my jeans and the blouse hanging over the top. In my pocket was Janet's old receipt.

I smiled at the security guard at the door as I passed him on my way in. Then I headed for the jeans display and located the pair I wanted. Before long, I spotted a nearby vacant cash register and counter and walked over and stood nonchalantly there for a few minutes. When I was sure no one was looking, I reached under and grabbed an empty bag.

Then it was back to the jeans. I picked up my size to study them, looked around, and slipped them into the empty bag. Then I pulled out Janet's receipt and the stapler and snapped it twice. With the stapler hidden back in my old jeans, I headed for the front door.

When I approached the security guard, I simply held my package so he could see the sales receipt on it. He didn't look to see if the contents matched the receipt. He smiled and waved me on, and I was out the door and quickly on my way back to the halfway house.

Back there, I went to my room and tried on my new jeans. They fit perfectly. And then, as I strutted around the room, I had the same mixed emotions again. Pride that I had pulled off a heist so easily— fear that I was still on the same one-way track back to jail.

I kept looking for a job. Something was going to have to give, pretty soon. Sure, the halfway house would keep me as long as I wanted to stay, but it was with the understanding that I pay my room and board—and my bill was mounting up and up. Would I ever be able to catch up?

Still no luck with jobs. Then one day I was sitting on the front porch, totally discouraged, when a car pulled up and stopped. A guy leaned out the window and yelled, "Hey, babe! Want to go for a ride?" That was the beginning of the second thing!

Was this guy wanting a prostitute? That's one thing I had not gotten into. The whole idea of it nauseated me. But maybe that was the way I was going to have to go. I had to get some money, somehow.

I got up and ambled toward the car. At least I could find out what he had in mind.

When he saw me coming, he got out and waited for me by the car. "I know you don't know me," he started, "but I'm a good friend of Janet's. What's your name?"

If the guy knew Janet, he must be okay, I decided. "My name's Sherri Lenier. What's yours?"

"Percy. Percy Wolten."

"Hi, Percy. Glad to get acquainted. Now what did you have in mind?"

"Well, Sherri, every so often I hire girls from the house for a special job. I was just wondering if maybe you were looking for work."

"Are you kidding? I've been looking all over this dumb town. Seems nobody trusts an ex-con—at least, not enough to hire one!"

"Yeah, I know how it is," he answered. "I'm on the level now, but, baby, I'm an ex-con, too."

"Well glory be! Sure is good to meet someone who is making it!"

Then I told him, in confidence, "Right now, I'm at the place where I'll do almost anything to earn a couple of bucks. You have something for me?"

"Yeah, I have a job," Percy answered with a big grin. "It'll take maybe four hours of your time, and it pays good money."

Four hours? Good money? That made me suspicious. He must be a pimp, looking for new girls for his stable.

"Percy, come on now; tell me why you really want me."

"Well, I'm in the selling business."

I had him now. "Sure," I said, "and your dad's the president of the company. You're just a dirty, stinking pimp, and the product you're going to sell is my body. Right?"

As I turned to walk back to the house, Percy grabbed my arm and wheeled me around. "Hey, girl, I've done a lot of bad things in my life, but that's one thing I haven't done. I have a little bit of respectability. I just wish you wouldn't make accusations until you understand what I'm talking about. Okay?"

Now it was my turn to be embarrassed. "Okay, Percy. I'm sorry. What's your game?"

"I can't go into the details now. But tomorrow I'll meet you at this address." He jotted it down on a scrap of paper and handed it to me. "Come at ten in the morning. You don't need references or anything like that. The first day should be pretty easy."

"Percy, this sounds too good to be true. Are you on the level?"

"Listen, baby, it's like I told you. I've been where you were. Two years ago, I got out after doing ten in the slammer. And, baby, it took me over a year to find a decent job. But I finally made it. Now I want to give other ex-cons a chance—since nobody else will. Baby, you're the lucky one. I just saw you there and decided you looked like someone who would appreciate a little help and wouldn't try to take advantage of me. Is it a deal?"

"Okay, Percy, I'll be there at ten sharp. You can count on me. And, Percy—thanks. I needed a friend!"

He smiled and headed back to his car. I was jumping for joy on the inside and skipped back to the house like a little girl who'd just made the boys' baseball team. I finally had a job!

Inside the house, I had to share my good news with someone. Why not Janet? After all, Percy said he was a friend of Janet's. So I hurried to her room.

"Guess what, Janet. I got a job! A guy named Percy Wolten just came by. He said he knew you. I'm going to start working for him tomorrow. Isn't that great?"

I was practically dancing around her room.

"Percy Wolten, you say? Percy? Percy? I can't recall anyone by that name."

Then, seeing the corners of my mouth drop, she hastened to add: "But then, I meet a lot of guys. Probably met him in a bar somewhere."

"Well, he sure seemed to know you, Janet. I'm sure I got his name right: Percy Wolten."

I think she sensed I needed some reassurance, for she told me, "Well, Sherri, every so often some kind citizen will come by and offer one of the girls a job. I guess you finally hit on that streak of good luck."

"He sure sounded legitimate," I said, trying to convince myself as much as her. "I'm to meet him tomorrow morning at ten. He gave me the address on a piece of paper. He must be legitimate, or he wouldn't have written down an address, would he?"

Janet responded, "That sure sounds legit to me. But if it doesn't work out, I know something else will turn up for you."

Later I talked to another of the girls, who had been there awhile, about that address. "Oh, that's only about six blocks or so from here," she said. "You can walk there easily. I'm not sure what building or anything, but it's in the downtown area."

I found it hard to sleep that night; I was so excited about having a job. Now I could really be out on my own!

About 9:30 the next morning, I started to walk on down to 437 Commercial Avenue, the address Percy had written on the paper. I sure didn't want to be late for my first day at work!

I walked the six blocks in twenty minutes. Four hundred thirty-seven Commercial Avenue was a huge office building, and I didn't know which office or which floor to go to. I walked in the main door and asked a security guard for Percy Wolten's office. The guard said he'd never heard of him.

That's strange! I thought. *Why would he give me the wrong address?* Suddenly the whole deal began to smell fishy. Was he really on the level?

I didn't know what else to do, so I wandered out onto the sidewalk, deciding to stay there at least until 10:00. Maybe Percy would still show up.

Right at 10:00, a car pulled up in front of where I was standing. It was Percy! He motioned for me to get in.

Two other men were sitting in the backseat, but I really didn't think too much about that. I was really glad to see Percy.

"Hey, what gives?" I asked as he eased away from the curb. "The security guard told me you don't have an office in that building."

Percy laughed. "Now, I didn't tell you I had an office there, did I? All I said was for you to meet me at that address. We usually pick our help up in front of a building like that. It's easier."

We were driving out of the downtown area, and Percy explained: "Sherri, I have a sales organization, and I'm going to teach you how to sell. We're going out to a suburban shopping center, and I'll tell you how it's done."

I'd never sold anything before, but I was willing to learn, I told him.

At this huge shopping center, we parked in front of J. C. Penneys.

Percy flipped off the key and turned toward me. "Are you ready to make a quick hundred bucks?" he asked.

"Yeah, man!" I responded. "How?"

"Well, Sherri, if you can make a good sale on this one, I'll show you how to make a thousand bucks in a day!"

Sounded as if he had robbing banks in mind!

"Now whatever you make, we all make," Percy went on. "We always split it four ways. That's part of the arrangement."

He reached over and chucked me under the chin with his finger. "Sherri, baby, we're going to get you out of that nasty old halfway house and set you up in a nice apartment. From today on, everything is going to start going your way. Okay?"

He made it sound too good. Something had to be wrong with a deal like this!

"Now here's what this is all about," Percy said. "In the trunk of this car is a microwave oven: very expensive. Also, we have a mixer that cost a bundle. All you have to do is to walk into Penneys and tell them you want your money back for these products."

That told me immediately what was up. These three guys would steal these items and then return them for credit.

No way was I going to get mixed up in another dishonest scheme. I was looking for legitimate work, not trying to get mixed up with another gang of crooks!

I reached for the door handle. I just had to get away. But Percy anticipated my actions and grabbed my arm and twisted it.

"Now, now, Sherri; let's level with each other. You know that your chances of finding a job are almost nil. Like I told you, I've been through this whole thing. I can't get work, and I have a wife and two kids to support. My two friends back there are in the same boat. Now take a look at that big company over there. They have bundles of money. It isn't going to hurt them one bit, to part with a little of it. We have the perfect setup here, so listen carefully."

"Now you listen to me," I countered. "I don't want any part of this. I've been through this route, and I'm trying to get out of the hole!"

"You don't know what a hole you're in!" Percy responded.

The two big guys in back let out with, "Yeah!"—the first words I had heard out of them all morning.

Percy went on: "Either you go in there and do what I tell you, or we're going to drive outside of town. When we get through with you, kid, you won't be able to walk. You won't be able to see. In fact, we'll probably just have to drop your body into the river. You get what I mean?"

I looked at Percy, then I looked at those two bruisers in the backseat. I was trapped! At least I had to look as if I were going along with them.

"Okay, I'll do it. But what's my story when I walk in there?"

"Very simple," Percy said. "You tell them you just got married, and these were wedding gifts, so you haven't any receipts for them. Here." He reached into his pocket. "Here's a gold wedding band. Wear it with pride—even if it is hot!"

The two guys in the back thought that was a riot, but I was scared to death. They wanted me to rip off Penneys. I didn't know if I could do it, but somehow I'd sure like to rip off these three guys. I sure didn't owe them anything!

It took both those big bruisers to unload the microwave oven from the trunk. Then I had to pick it up and carry it into the store. They loaded the mixer on top. As I staggered toward the front door, the three of them disappeared. Fortunately a man ahead of me saw my predicament and held the door open. Then he showed me where the appliance department was—at the back of the store.

My arms were killing me. I kept bumping into people, who looked daggers at me. But no one offered to help, and I finally stumbled up to the service desk in the appliance department and said, "Wow! I didn't think I was going make it back here! These gifts must weigh a ton!"

The woman just glanced at me. "I got married a week ago, and I have all kinds of gifts," I continued. "Would you believe I got two microwave ovens and two mixers? I found out these came from Penneys, so I've come to return them and get my money back. Is that possible?"

I knew clerks usually aren't very excited about handling exchanges, but she just kept on staring. So I flashed the wedding ring and asked, "Lady, do you make exchanges here at the store?"

"Yes," she finally answered, "we do make exchanges—if you have a receipt."

"Maybe you didn't hear me," I replied. "I said these were wedding gifts. Naturally I don't have any receipts."

I started looking around for the nearest door, in case I had to run. That's when I spotted Percy looking at TV sets. Then I saw the other two guys over in the sports department, looking at golf clubs. I guess they were going to make sure I didn't get the money and split.

"Just a minute," the lady was saying. "I'll have to check with the store manager on this. It gets to be a little bit of a problem, when you don't have a receipt."

I was about to decide this was a good time for me to break and run. Percy must have read my thoughts, for he walked to the middle of the aisle and stood there— between me and the door—with his arms folded.

I waited. In a couple of minutes, the woman came back with the manager—a real short guy who seemed to enjoy his authority. "Ma'am," he said to me, "we'll have to have a receipt before we can exchange these. Couldn't you call your friends and ask them for a receipt?"

"Are you kidding?" I exploded. "Now tell me, sir, if you got married, would you want to call up people who were nice enough to send you a gift and ask them for a receipt? Why, I couldn't do that! That would be too embarrassing!"

"Yeah, I guess you're right," he admitted reluctantly.

"Do you have any identification?"

Oh, no! The only identification I had with me was my social-security card. I thought I was going to need it for my new job! So I told him that was all I had and that my brother had driven me over.

"I see," he responded. "Maybe if I filled out some of these forms . . . ." His voice trailed off.

He sure was making it hard on me!

"Your name, please," he said.

I'd better give a false one. "Sherri Upson," I answered. The Sherri would match my Social-Security card. I could say that Upson was my married name and that I hadn't had time to get the card changed yet. I congratulated myself on thinking so fast under pressure.

"And your address?"

Better make that false, too. "Four hundred twenty-six Abbot Street, Teaneck, New Jersey."

"Okay," he responded. "If you'll just come with me, maybe we can take care of this."

He stepped from behind the counter and grabbed my arm as he led me to a back office. Wasn't it strange for him to take my arm?

No sooner had he ushered me into that room than I heard him say, "Ma'am, you're under arrest. That address you gave me is false."

Through a window in the door, I could see Percy and the other two guys take off toward the main entrance. they must have known I was nailed.

I tried to make all sorts of excuses about the address. Finally the little guy told me he really wasn't the manager; he was the store detective. The oven and the mixer had been stolen from the store, and they were waiting to see if someone tried to bring them back for a refund. He said this had been happening to a number of stores in the area. Apparently Percy had really milked this trick.

Two cops came at his call, and they asked more questions. I wasn't about to admit anything, so they handcuffed me and took me down and booked me. Then they put me in a cell.

This was a filthy jail, with rats running around the floor! I was scared to death that while I slept, one of them would start gnawing at my toes or even my face. I'd seen other prisoners with bloody scars from where the rats had been gnawing on them. The very thought of it both terrified me and made me sick to my stomach!

Besides the rats, there were other girls in this cell. Their talk was absolutely filthy—and some of them were, too. A couple of them were winos, vomiting all over themselves and everything else.

The whole situation made me so upset that I started vomiting, too. The mess in that cell was indescribable!

The next morning they brought breakfast, if you could call it that: cold coffee and hard bread. I passed it by. Nothing had been done to clean up yesterday's vomit.

Later that day, they brought in three lesbians. I shuddered as they looked me over. Now I had to watch out for them attacking me, too.

When they booked me, they said that I was allowed one phone call. It wouldn't do any good to call the halfway house. They didn't have the authority to do anything. I had no other friends. My parents? They didn't want anything to do with me. So my one phone call did me absolutely no good.

That afternoon, some detectives pulled me out of the cell for more questions. I decided if I cooperated, maybe I'd get off easier. After all, I'd been duped into doing what I'd been arrested for!

First, the detectives wanted to know who the guys were in this caper. When I told them Percy Wolten, they laughed. They said the last girl they booked worked for a Percy Wolten.

Then one of them told me, "I don't know what's the matter with you girls. You're so gullible. These dudes know about halfway houses. They know you girls are uptight when you can't get jobs. So you're easy prey."

I knew I was going to have to suffer the consequences for this crime. They had nailed me with the goods. Oh, was there no way I could escape from this revolving door of crime? Even when I tried to go straight, I couldn't.

I pled guilty at the trial. My court-assigned lawyer was a young guy who was really smart. He told the judge about how I was duped into this. The judge listened sympathetically.

When I heard the verdict announced, I could scarcely believe it. "Six months," the judge said. I was expecting ten years!

I headed back to prison with mixed feelings. It would be better than that filthy cell I'd been in, but it was still prison, and any prison is a hellhole.

When they got me there, I went through induction. It never is pleasant: the physical checks, the abuse, the system—they're all dehumanizing. Then they led me to my cell.

As I walked into that cold, damp, dirty cell, I felt as if the bottom had fallen out of my life. I was a loser. I went over to a corner and cried like I've never cried before.

I knew that now I had absolutely no future. I'd been to prison before; now I was back. I would always be known as an ex-con. I was one of those statistics— those habitual criminals who are never able to make it on the outside.

At my age, was that all I had to look forward to— being in and out of prison? Talk about feeling hopeless and helpless! Here I was totally trapped, my life forever messed up by my stupidity and greed.

Why was I ever born? I sobbed. *And who cares about me? I might as well be dead!*

I shuddered at the word *dead!* But I couldn't get it out of my mind. If I killed myself, would that be the end of all my troubles? But was that really the way out? Did death end it all? Or somewhere was there a God to meet; a God I had heard about a few times? I wondered.

12

I was so torn up by the raw deal I had that I just couldn't adjust to prison life again. I refused to eat. They threatened me with solitary confinement. So what? I would just as soon die.

After lockup one night, I stretched out on my bunk. Sleep was far from my eyes, as I went over and over how stupid I had been to let Percy dupe me.

As the guard walked by, he threw something in, and it hit the cell floor with a thump. It scared me half to death. What was it? Food? But I still wasn't hungry. They weren't going to tempt me to eat by throwing things in through the bars, like you would to an animal in the zoo!

He just walked on by, without saying anything. Well, my curiosity finally got the best of me. I just had to see what he had thrown in, so I rolled off my bunk and picked up the package. Only it wasn't a package. It was a book.

Attractive cover, I thought. It showed a girl—maybe about my age. She looked like she was into prostitution, the way she was dressed.

The book was called *Cindy.* I didn't know anybody by that name. It was written by John Benton. That name didn't ring a bell, either. But the pages of the book were well-worn; obviously quite a number of people had read it. What did I have to lose? I might as well sit down on my bunk and thumb through it.

Well, before long I was reading, for the story

grabbed me. It was about this young girl in New York City who had become a junkie. *The dummy,* I thought. At least I had been smart enough to stay off that road!

I read on and on in the dim light, fascinated with the story of Cindy's life and how she had to face one crisis after another. Wondering how it could possibly come out, I read on. That's where I learned about all the beautiful ways God had changed Cindy's life when she trusted in Him. The book told about how she had gone to a place in upstate New York—the Walter Hoving Home, it was called. I learned that the author of the book was in charge of that home for girls who have had problems with drugs, prostitution, alcohol, and so on.

It was so exciting to read how God had brought hope into Cindy's life and changed things completely for her. I wondered if God could help me.

But I already knew the answer to that. No way! I was a loser, a condemned prison inmate. I would be in and out of prison for the rest of my life. No way God or the devil could get me out of this mess. No, there was absolutely no hope for me!

I couldn't sleep after I finished *Cindy.* I just lay there with the book on my chest, thinking.

Cindy had been in prison, too. She had thought her life was hopeless, too. And she had even been a junkie. But the book told about her being born again, about her life being changed because she did something it explained as "accepting Jesus Christ as her Saviour."

I knew a little about that. Our neighbors, the Haleys, had taken me to Sunday school when I was quite young. I didn't remember much that I learned, but I remember one teacher kept on saying that Jesus loved me. Even then, I thought that was great. I needed to be loved by somebody!

That started me reviewing all the terrible things that had happened to me. If only things had been different. If only I had made some different choices. Maybe if I had been born into a different family—a family like the Haleys—my life would have purpose and hope.

Then I wondered, *Is there such a thing as a real, loving Saviour?* Did Jesus really love me?

Oh, if only my folks had gone to church with the Haleys, when they asked them to. Maybe then I would have had a chance.

But no use worrying about all those *if only*s. I'd messed up my life beyond any hope. I didn't have a friend in the world. No one cared if I lived or died.

Even if I killed myself, no one would attend my funeral!

Well, that really brought a flood of tears!

I don't really know what happened next, except I heard myself talking to God: "God, I don't know if You're really up there; and I sure don't know if You know I'm down here. I know I don't deserve any favors or anything like that, but if You could do what You did for Cindy, do You think You could do a little for me? I mean, could You help me? If anybody needs help, I do!"

The tears kept coming—for how long, I really don't know. The next thing I remember, it was morning, and I was sleepy!

That was the morning we were told to expect an inspection. A judge was visiting the prison. We were all to clean up our cells and put some smiles on our faces! What a farce! But we all knew better than to

protest. If we acted up while we had visitors, that
would mean solitary or removal of some privileges.
They knew how to make life miserable for us!

That afternoon we were locked in our cells, awaiting
the inspection.

I noticed about five people coming toward me. I
always hated it when I was behind bars and people
came peering in at me. But when I looked at the group,
I was sure I recognized one man. Was it? Could it be?
Yes, it was! It was Judge Walker—the judge Lillian
and I had stolen the guns from. He had given me a
break that first time.

When he passed my cell, I called, "Judge Walker.
May I talk to you a minute?"

He stopped. "Yes?" he asked.

"Don't you remember me, sir?"

He studied me. "No, I'm very sorry, but I don't.
Perhaps you've been in my court. Well, young lady,
it's been my responsibility to put quite a few young
ladies away, and I'm afraid I don't remember them
all."

"Judge, I'll bet if I told you why I was brought before you, you'd remember."

He smiled.

"Do you remember when two girls stole a bunch of
guns from your house? Well, I was one of those girls.
I'm Sherri Lenier."

"Oh, of course! How could I forget? But you were a
little younger then. I remember another thing about
that case: There was a fence involved. I think his name
was Willie. Well, we caught him, and eventually he
turned state's evidence. He's serving time now, but we
sure cleaned up a bunch of people on that case—even

one in the police department!''

Then he looked me right in the eye. "As I remember, Sherri, you solemnly promised me that
you'd go straight. What happened?''

"Well, sir, I did go straight through the rest of high
school. I got a job after I graduated, and then I was
laid off and couldn't find work. The bills were piling
up, and my roommate and I found that stealing brought
us in some easy money. Well, they caught me, and I
served a two-year sentence for that one.''

He was listening sympathetically.

"Well, when I got out," I told him, "I went to a
halfway house. I couldn't get work again. Finally I
became a sucker for three guys who had some hot
merchandise. I tried to exchange it at Penneys, and I
got nailed. I did wrong. I know that. So I tried to
cooperate with them, and I pleaded guilty. I had a kind
judge, and he gave me only six months. I guess you
gentlemen do have kind hearts now and then, don't
you?''

He laughed at that one. "Well, not many people
would say that! But we're just ordinary human beings.
I try to do my best to give justice to all. Remember, I
tried to give you a chance, because it was your first
offense. Well, I think God wants me to believe in
people.''

His mention of God reminded me of Cindy. She had
come to trust God, too. Would Judge Walker know
something about God that might answer some of my
questions?

"It's strange that you mentioned God, Judge
Walker. Are you a Christian?''

"Yes, I sure am!" he answered quickly. "And I'm

not ashamed for anyone to know it.''

The group was getting a little edgy and started to
walk off. I wanted to say something else, but the judge
interrupted. ''Well, it's been good talking to you again,
Sherri. I'm going to ask my church to pray for you. I
thought you had some good potential when you came
before me years ago. I think I can still see that potential.''

And with a wave, he was gone.

I turned and walked back to my bunk. There sat the
book *Cindy*. I remembered my prayer last night. Was
God really answering my prayer? Or was it just a coincidence that Judge Walker came by and I found out he,
too, was a Christian? Maybe it did just happen, but it
was a little unusual!

I didn't have long to think about it, for a few minutes
later, a guard came and unlocked my cell.

''Those people taking the tour have asked to talk to
some of the inmates privately,'' he explained. ''Judge
Walker wants to see you. I noticed you talking to him
before, and I don't know what you said to him, but
let's get something straight, Sherri Lenier. Don't tell
any phony stories. Don't exaggerate the conditions
here. Because if you create any problems for us, we
have our ways of dealing with troublemakers! You understand?''

''Yes, sir!'' I responded. ''What I want to talk to
Judge Walker about isn't going to create any problems
around here!''

The guard led me down a corridor and into a room.
No one was there. He motioned for me to sit down,
then he went out.

In a few minutes, Judge Walker entered. ''Sherri,''

he started, "I'm not going to talk to you about conditions in this penitentiary. I'm well aware of them. They're not good. But there's not much I can do about them, either. I find it's good public relations for me to visit here occasionally. I am able to maintain a greater sense of justice, when I take these tours. And I am able to warn young offenders about what they are going to have to face, if they continue in a life of crime."

I dropped my head.

"The real reason I wanted to talk to you," he went on, "is to try to encourage you. When I walked away from your cell a few minutes ago, God spoke to my heart about you. He seemed to be telling me He was trying to get through to you. Have you felt God near you recently?"

I then told the judge what I have already told you—how a guard threw a copy of the book *Cindy* into my cell last night and how I had read it until the wee hours this morning. I mentioned how Cindy had found help at a place called the Walter Hoving Home.

When I mentioned the Walter Hoving Home, Judge Walker interrupted. "Oh, I know that place. We have a man in the probation department—Matt Rocco—who has sent a number of girls up there to Brother Benton and his staff. I understand they have a tremendous staff and tremendous program, and they really show the love of Jesus. They teach the girls from the Bible. I know that after a year in their program, many of the girls have gone on to be fantastic young ladies, with places of responsibility in society. They really amount to something in life!"

I'd never heard about any kind of a program like that before. The only thing I knew about was the halfway

house where I'd been. They were kind, well-meaning
people there, but they didn't do much to help me.
Finding a job wasn't the total answer for an ex-con—
and they hadn't even helped me find a job. Really all
they had done was give me a place to live. And they
expected me to pay for that.

I told the judge it sounded really exciting.

"Well, Sherri," he said, "if you're interested in
something like that, I might be able to see what I can
do for you. At least I'll talk to Mr. Rocco. He might
have some suggestions. Since your sentence is only for
six months, things could turn out better for you."

I couldn't believe what he was telling me. Was there
really hope for me? Maybe God really did listen to my
prayer last night. Wow! There really must be a God!

"I must go now," Judge Walker said as he stood up.
"But I'll put someone in touch with you. However,
you must be patient. These things take time. And I
promise you—I won't forget you. I keep my prom-
ises!"

He grinned at his cleverness, and then he was gone.

13

I waited for four days, after that visit with Judge Walker. Then a guard came to take me to the visiting area. He said a probation officer wanted to see me.

Matt Rocco was an absolute delight. He explained all about the Walter Hoving Home, first. He told me all about their beautiful, thirty-seven-acre estate and mansion in Garrison, New York, and how it was funded by Christian people all over the United States who were interested in helping girls like me.

Then he told me about their work program and their Bible studies. Hundreds of girls had come to the home and were changed by giving their lives to Christ and studying the Bible, he said. Even junkies were delivered from the power of drug addition by a greater power—the power of Jesus Christ.

"Would you like to go there, Sherri?" he asked.

Go? It sounded like a dream! "Of course, I'd love to go!" I told him. "But how are you going to spring me out of here?"

He laughed. "Hey, I'm on the right side of the law," he said. "But you have a real friend in Judge Walker. He has a little influence, in cases like this. Maybe we could work something through the courts, so you could be placed on probation. If you do really well at the Walter Hoving Home, the courts will count that as part of your sentence."

He rubbed his chin thoughtfully. "I don't know. It's a long shot, Sherri, but let's you and I agree together

177

in prayer. We'll pray for God's will."

"Do you believe God really answers prayer, Mr. Rocco?"

"Of course I do, Sherri. You're not the first case I've worked with. For many years now, I've been sending girls up to the Walter Hoving Home. And I want you to know that some of those girls today are among the most beautiful Christians you ever could meet. Why, some of them are in Bible schools. Some are married to ministers! And others are out in society, being what Christ wants them to be. It all started when they turned their lives over to Jesus Christ."

He looked straight into my eyes. "Sherri, how about you? Would you like to give your life to Christ?"

"I sure would, Mr. Rocco. I really need help. But how do I go about it?"

"Well, it's really very simple," he explained. "Here, let me just read you some verses from the Bible." He pulled a Bible out of his attaché case.

"The Bible shows you how to give your life to Jesus," he went on. "The first thing a person must do is very simply acknowledge that he or she is a sinner. That's not too hard to do, is it?"

I laughed. Embarrassed, I said, "Oh, please excuse me. I didn't mean to laugh. But I would think that everybody knows they're sinners. I certainly have been a sinner—a real bad sinner. My sins have put me behind bars."

"Well, that's what I'm talking about," Mr. Rocco said. "There's something inside of everybody— whether we're in a prison or outside—that says we're sinners. The Bible puts it this way: 'For all have sinned and come short of the glory of God.' That's Romans, chapter three, verse twenty-three." He showed me what he had just read.

"So the first step is to recognize that you're a sinner," Mr. Rocco said. "The second thing is to confess your sins to God.

"The Bible says, 'If we confess our sins, he is faithful and just to forgive us our sins, and to cleanse us from all unrighteousness.' That's First John, chapter one, verse nine. So the second step is simple, too. Just ask God to forgive your sins."

"It really sounds easy," I said. "Can it really be that simple?"

"It really is!" he answered. "In fact, it is so simple that even children can understand it and do it.

"Now, Sherri, here's the third step. After you've asked Jesus to forgive your sins, then invite Him into your heart. When you do, He's promised to come in and live within you."

"Aw, come on, Mr. Rocco. I don't mean to be irreverent or anything like that, but can you honestly say that really works? I mean, for someone like me, who seriously thought of killing herself in this prison? Besides, you know my record. I'm a thief."

He flipped over the pages of his Bible and showed me a passage in the Gospel of Luke, chapter 23. "It's the familiar story of the thief on the cross," he said. "Remember? When Jesus died for the sins of the world, He was put to death between two thieves. One of those thieves made fun of Jesus. The other one was sorry for his sins and said, 'Lord, remember me when You come into Your kingdom.' Jesus promised that thief that he would be with Him in Paradise that very day! So no matter what you've done, Sherri, if you confess your sins to Jesus, He'll forgive you.''

He closed the Bible and looked straight into my eyes again. ''I'll tell you what, Sherri. Why don't you, if you want to—and this has to be strictly on your own— just simply pray in your own words what I've just said? Tell Jesus you're a sinner, ask Him to forgive your sins, and then by faith say you receive Him into your heart. If you do that, the Bible says that you're saved. That means you're born again—a brand-new person in Jesus. Then God will look at your heart—and not just at what you're saying—and it will become a fact.

''Now when you do this, you may feel different. Or maybe you won't. Some people immediately feel happy all over. Others feel absolutely nothing. But that doesn't make any difference. We don't go by our feelings; we go by faith. We've done what God's Word tells us to do. We believe it—that's the faith part of it. And we are saved!''

''Well,'' I answered, ''when I go to chapel next Sunday here in the prison, I'll try to remember it and go through with it. Okay?''

''Of course, that's a possibility,'' he said. ''But did you know you don't have to wait to go to chapel? Jesus can come into your heart right here and now!''

''You mean we don't have to be in church? Can this happen while you and I are sitting right here, on these chairs, and talking?''

''Absolutely! It's happened to millions of other people all over the world, in all kinds of places and situations. And it can happen to you *right now!*''

''Wow! This is too good to be true! Okay. Here goes!''

I glanced, to see what his reaction to that was. He had bowed his head and closed his eyes, so I did that, too. Then I said, "Dear Lord, I'm a sinner—a real bad sinner. I'm here in this place because I deserve to be here. I have committed all kinds of sins. So please forgive me of all my sins.

"Now, Lord, Mr. Rocco said I was to receive You by faith. That's what I do right now. I receive You into my heart. Please, Lord Jesus, come into my heart right now. Amen."

I looked up, and Mr. Rocco was smiling.

"Sherri, according to the prayer you just prayed, where is Jesus right now—if you prayed that prayer in faith?"

"Well," I responded, "I asked Him to come into my heart. So Jesus is in my heart."

He slapped his knee. "That's right, Sherri! He's in your heart. And what's more, He wants to live there for the rest of your life. Jesus wants to change your world for the better. He said He came to give life, and that more abundantly. That's His purpose—to give you abundant life."

"You mean Jesus is really in my heart—right this minute?"

"That's right, Sherri. The Bible also says, 'Christ *in you* the hope of glory.' He's right within your heart now!"

"Wow!" I responded. "That's really exciting! Now what?"

"That's a good question," he said. "The Bible talks about what happened to you as being born again. That means you're just like a newborn baby. You need to learn to grow as a Christian. That means you'll need to read the Bible. It becomes our spiritual food. As we begin to live according to what it teaches, then we grow as Christians. A lot of people forget to use the Bible to guide them through life. It's got many wonderful things to teach us.

"And you should also pray. Prayer is talking to God. Reading the Bible is letting God talk to us."

He handed me his Bible. "Here, Sherri. I want you to have this."

Then he told me to read from the Gospel of Matthew, the third, fourth, fifth, and sixth chapters. Especially, he said, I was to pay attention to what Jesus taught His disciples in the Sermon on the Mount.

I was so thrilled to have my own Bible—the first one I'd ever owned.

We talked some more after that, and he told me he'd stay in touch. He had no idea if he could get my early release, he said, but he'd certainly pray for God's will.

"I can't guarantee anything," he told me, "but I've seen God work miracles before, and I am going to believe for one for you!"

It wasn't hard for me to believe in miracles now, because I had just experienced one. Jesus was living in my heart! That was the beginning of a lot of changes.

14

When I got back to my cell, I had this allover feeling that something good was about to happen to me. It did, but not exactly in the way I expected.

That night I read the Bible for the first time, and what Jesus said became important for me to learn and to live.

I wish I could say that I was out of prison the next day. It didn't happen that way. The process took three months. But I can honestly say that I've never known three months to go by so quickly.

The days seemed different now. The prison had changed. No, I knew it really hadn't; I was the one who had changed. I really was born again. I figured out that if Jesus was in my heart, that meant He was right in that prison cell with me, helping me.

As I prayed and read and studied the Bible, I was able to take anything that prison threw at me. I mean anything!

I began to tell the other girls what had happened to me. Some were eager to listen, and I shared my faith in Christ with them. Some of them started going to chapel. One of them was born again, too, and we used to study the Bible together whenever we could.

Finally my release date came, and I was immediately transferred to the Walter Hoving Home.

When I was driven onto those beautiful grounds, I was overwhelmed! Imagine a poor kid like me, one from the wrong side of the tracks, getting to live in a mansion for a whole year! It was like my childhood dreams come true!

When I met the staff, I was even more over-whelmed. They were all so good and so kind and so helpful, and yet they were all so serious about what they were doing.

The girls who were in the program welcomed me with open arms. I learned they had been through the same kinds of things I had been through. They knew how to sympathize with my problems and when to encourage me to stand on my own feet. I just couldn't get over the love the girls and the staff had for me. It was almost too good to be true. But it was true!

I immediately adjusted to the schedule and was eager to learn more about the Bible and what God expected of me.

After I had been there for three months, I came across one lesson that I guess I wasn't too eager to learn. It was on how to build family relationships and get over bitterness. I was supposed to make a list of twenty good things about my father and mother.

I was totally stumped. But as I thought about it and prayed about it, I remembered that my mother had to go through the valley of the shadow of death to bring me into this world. Then I remembered that cheese sandwich she fixed me, and how she really had been concerned about me—and suddenly I had a long, long list. I even remembered a few good things about my father. He did work and bring home money so we could have food, and one time when I was very sick, he brought me a soda to settle my stomach. He sat by my bed and rubbed my back. And when I was little, he used to read me stories . . . .

Yes, my folks did have some good qualities about them.

Then the clincher came. I had to write them a letter and apologize for not being the daughter God intended me to be! It was hard, but I did it.

I guess I really didn't expect an answer, so I was shocked when Mother phoned. She said she couldn't believe all that had happened to me. She and Dad were anxious to come and visit me, she said.

That Saturday afternoon, they arrived. Without hesitation, I threw my arms aroumd my mother. That was easy. But I dreaded hugging my father. I knew I was going to smell that same old liquor smell. So I held my breath when I hugged him. He held me a long time, and I had to breathe. Surprise! No liquor on his breath! He was sober!

One of the girls offered them some coffee, so we went into the dining room and talked. I brought them up-to-date on all the things I had been through and about how God had helped me.

A little later, the director's wife, Mrs. Benton (we all call her Mom B.) joined us at the table. It didn't take her long to get around to why she joined us. She wanted to tell my parents how to receive Jesus as their Saviour.

I'd told Mom B. my parents weren't Christians. When she heard they were coming, she smiled that big smile of hers and said, "Well, they're coming to the right place!" People who come to the Walter Hoving Home, she said, are overwhelmed with the presence of Christ that they find there. That makes it easy for them to find Jesus as their Saviour.

Mom B. got right to the point, and I put in a word or

two about receiving Jesus. Then she asked them the
greatest question anybody could be asked: "Would
you like to receive Jesus as your Saviour?"

I expected them to make some excuse, but they both
said they were ready. When they got my letter, they
had talked to their neighbors, the Haleys, about Chris-
tianity. Now they couldn't get over the change in me
and the radiance in my face. "If Jesus can change
somebody that much," Dad said, "then I really need
Him and want Him."

"Me too!" Mom added.

So Mom B. explained from the Bible how to be
saved, and both my parents prayed the sinner's
prayer. Jesus forgave them of their sins. And in that
moment, we became a Christian family!

My folks came up frequently after that, to attend the
chapel services at the home on Sunday mornings. Dad
was always sober. He told everyone who would listen
that Jesus had taken away all his desire for liquor!
Another miracle!

One Sunday afternoon, Mom B. took my folks to
the prayer room. There they had the beautiful experience of being baptized with the Holy Spirit. I had had
that wonderful experience soon after I came to the
home. The Bible describes it as "joy unspeakable and
full of glory." And I had discovered that the Holy
Spirit within me gave me power to live the Christian
life. I wasn't trying to be good by the strength of my
own willpower. The Holy Spirit actually gave me the
power to help me please God and serve my fellowman!

Well, my year at the Walter Hoving Home just flew
by. Then it was time for graduation. As I reviewed the
year, it was absolutely unbelievable what God and I

had accomplished! Of course, He gets the credit. But I worked with Him.

I spent a few weeks at home and then headed for Bible school in Pennsylvania. That's where I am now. I don't know what I'm going to do after I graduate, but I do know the Lord has a beautiful plan for my life. He makes that plan plain to me as I trust and follow Him.

As you're reading my story, I don't know where you are. Maybe you're at home, reading late at night, or maybe you're in a jail cell, like I was. But no matter where you are, Jesus wants to change your life, too.

Maybe your life is in complete turmoil—one crisis after another—and you have no peace. But take it from someone who really knows that kind of a life, Jesus can give you peace. Since I decided, that day in the penitentiary, to give my life over to Jesus Christ, it's never been the same. He has made my life worth living. Believe me, that was the greatest decision I ever made. I'm praying that you'll make it, too—*right now!*

It's not difficult, you know.

All you have to do are the three things Mr. Rocco explained to me: Acknowledge you're a sinner, then ask Jesus to forgive your sins, and by simple faith receive Him into your heart.

After you've done that, pray and read your Bible. Study Christ's Sermon on the Mount. That's a good place to start. Then find a good church to attend—a church where they really teach the Bible. As you learn to grow in spiritual matters, you'll never be sorry. It's the only way to know real life!

Do it right now, okay? I'm praying for you—just as

the Haleys, I found out later, never quit praying for me!

I know God works miracles. He's done it for me. And I believe He's going to do one for you, too—*right now!*

Some good things are happening
at The Walter Hoving Home.

Dramatic and beautiful changes have been taking
place in the lives of many girls since the Home began
in 1967. Ninety-four percent of the graduates who
have come with problems such as narcotic addiction,
alcoholism and delinquency have found release and
happiness in a new way of living—with Christ. The
continued success of this work is made possible
through contributions from individuals who are concerned about helping a girl gain freedom from enslav-
ing habits. Will you join with us in this work by
sending a check?

The Walter Hoving Home
Box 194
Garrison, New York 10524
(914) 424-3674

Your Gifts Are Tax Deductible

The Walter Hoving Home.